Adam's writings, much like the man himself, are raw, poetic and simultaneously re him as courageous, a man willing to acknowledge his mistakes, a quality that makes and grounded. He and his book offer good medicine for those wanting to engage wit of living in a body on earth in these difficult times that offer us such an opportunity his work are a dance in themselves.

— Ya'Acov Darling Khan, Shaman, Best Selling Author and Co-Founder of Movement Medicine

Adam's writing clearly emerges from his deeply lived experience and practice. This is generous, sumptuous seriously helpful stuff. Rooted in bone deep experience, in the fires of the heart, honed in decades of practice. If you are a practitioner of movement as a transformative path, no matter what your chosen movement genre is, I'm sure this volume will accompany you in ways that help you integrate the good stuff and take it with you into he heart of your life. The words of this book taste good. In this book Adam is serving up a nourishing feast grown in the garden of his own experience, both as dancer and teacher.

— Susannah Darling Khan Co- Founder of Movement Medicine

Adam and I have bumped into each other on dance floors across the globe for over 30 years. His devotion to movement as an emotional and spiritual path is unwavering. Adam has lived every word of what he shares in this book.

— Lori Saltzman, teacher, mover, writer, co-founder of Open Floor International

Adam has more experience and gritty, free-spirited commitment to movement practice than pretty much anyone I know. This book is clear, funky and honest. It will be liquid gold for anyone who wants to discover or deepen how moving our bodies can change our lives in a multitude of real ways, from wild liberation to tender renewal.

— Christian de Sousa, Movement Facilitator & Artist

Adam writes as he teaches, with a simple wisdom that makes complete sense; a balm for over-complicated times. With his fierce no-bullshit honesty, his words are familiar, like a soul-whisper from the Self that says, 'You're doing great. Keep going.' The words on these pages jumped out and grabbed me, called me to action, inspired me to continue to show up for myself, my passions and the beautiful mystery of the big dance. You don't need to go to the mountains to pray. You can start right here and take the pathway home.

— David Juriansz, Director of Moving Essence

Pathways Home is an act of generosity from a seeker of self-truth and connection through conscious movement. Adam's generosity stems from his honesty, his unique voice in speaking of his many years of experience as dancer, facilitator, father, lover, friend, fighter. His essence translates onto the page full of dynamism, movement and humour – he knows if you're not doing his explorations ;-)

Adam sets up his stall clearly and with a soft, able confidence. The balance of personal experience, exercises and explorations and insights from a life-long practice and commitment to movement itself as the most true guide to self, is fine-tuned and beautifully choreographed. The book is expansive and inclusive of many conscious movement modalities, another act of generosity. It's an invitation from a passionate heart to dip your toe or submerge totally into the path of movement as practice. This book sparkles.

— Cathy Ryan, MA, Movement Facilitator, BISO Co-Founder and Open Floor Founding Member

Pathways Home is replete with detailed suggestions, pointers, encouragement and hard-earned insight into the benefits and potential obstacles to creating, sustaining or advancing personal practice in any movement modality. Adam's enthusiasm and intelligent attention to detail shine through, making it an inspiring and useful resource for anyone interested in the healing power of movement.

— Alain Allard, Founder of Moves Into Consciousness

For any one hungry for transformation, Adam makes movement practice as accessible as breathing and as important as saving ourselves and the planet. He is the real deal and he reminds us that we are all the real deal. His words dance with the depth of his own discipline, curiosity and down to earth passion.

— Meredith Davies, Dancer, Mother and Director of Moving Essence

A poignant, poetic and practical collection of reflections and wisdom. His simple and encouraging steps resonated in me so much that I needed to put down the book every so often to get up and move!

— Christa Cocciole, Body Oriented Systemic Therapist, Social Activist and Transformation Midwife

Adam's wealth of experience and his fierce courage to share personal stories will inspire you to move forward on your own path of evolution.

— Bettina Rothe, Embodied Leadership Coach, 5Rhythms Movement Facilitator

Brimming with care and confidence. Adam gives you straight-up clear statements, directives, and knowledge about his life long practice: dancing. Read this and then burn it.

— Vincent Martinez-Grieco, Designer of Soul Motion, and of Next Steps

An inspired guide to assist the novice and experienced movement practitioner create a robust and meaningful home practice. With rich story telling and helpful shortcuts, Pathways Home will deepen your connection to the dancing path.

— Amber Ryan, Co-Founder of The 360 Emergence

Adam Barley's book offers us a detailed day to day skill set to begin the primary function of being alive: Embodied living as the key to being here. For the beginner or the advanced practitioner it is a signpost for the road home to the body, our one true address.

— Kate Shela, Co-Founder of The 360 Emergence

Adam is a deeply soulful, thoughtful and poetic teacher that I have known for years and trust deeply. This book will give you a glimpse inside his big heart.

— Mark Walsh, Director of Embodiment Unlimited, author of Embodiment - Moving Beyond Mindfulness

I highly recommend this practical gem for anyone curious about movement as a practice. The discipline and dedication that Adam shares comes straight from his own experience and will open doors of what is possible for you.

— Amara Pagano, Founder of Azul movement practice

Adam is a scavenger and investigator, a relentless lover of spelling it out and breaking it down in accessible enticing ways. This book is an invitation to try it on and give it a go because, with the state of our planet, why wouldn't you?

— Deborah Jay-Lewin, Founding Member of Open Floor International

Adam speaks from a wealth of embodied experience, and his passionate wisdom dances throughout the pages with a pristine sense of clarity. This book will enliven your creativity and spark joy in your everyday step. Enjoy the dance!

— Davida Taurek, Psychotherapist, 5Rhythms Facilitator, Mindfulness Coach

Pathways Home

First Edition 2022

This book has been printed using matte paper for environmental reasons.

Ordering information: adambarley.com

Cover Art: Devir

Created by Rui Miguel

Illustration credits appear on p158,
which constitutes an extension of this copyright page.

Designed by csidesign.co.uk

Introduction: Pathways

Work on your stuff, or your stuff will work on you. — Steven Forrest

A family holiday with my kids, my parents, and my brother's family too. As often happens in such situations, I find myself compelled to look after everybody else, ignoring my own needs and shoving myself into a corner with less and less space as the days go by. Preparing an evening meal, with everyone bustling around, I am at bursting point.

Filled with seething resentment, and awash with shame about the inappropriate extent of that, I know I have to do something. I manage to get out of the back door onto the lawn outside. It's raining, it's dark, and I don't care. I stagger around the garden, writhing like Medusa and growling at the undergrowth. Five minutes is enough; I am back in my own centre, grounded in my own feet instead of everyone else's, and can go back into the fray with a little more equanimity.

Movement has been my thing for over three decades now. I have writhed in hell until it became as satisfying as a hearty meal, and soared so high to the heavens I could see all the world spread out below me. I have been bored, scared shitless, turned on, inspired, and apoplectic with rage. I have laughed aloud and wept buckets. I have met myself face to face as an embodied experience: using fingers, toes and backbone, all sweat and deep breaths.

Many of my more extreme experiences have been in groups, rocking it out to loud music, but on most days my practice time has been alone, at home. Or in the forest, or on a mountainside. On the beach. Across all those dance floors, repeated solo practice has grown into the bedrock of my being. And although it has often not been so dramatic as the group-work, there have been some experiences so astonishing, touching or strange that I shall never forget them.

Day by day, the ordinariness of this practice has quietly nourished a strength in me that is both down to earth and unusual – a kind of grounded ability to go through difficult stuff and make something of it. I do not believe I could have found that strength in any number of workshops, self-help books or therapy sessions. I have a relationship with movement that is nothing to do with any teacher or method but comes from my own breath and body, and the mysterious One that is within us all.

This book is to encourage you to do the same, because the truth is I couldn't have managed the family moment I described above without a solid practice already in place. We have to practise when we don't need it, so that it's there when we do. I have poured my heart through my moving body so many times that it's become second nature.

Movement practice is not only my go-to rescue package when I'm struggling with life though. It's the way I get rooted in my body, open my heart, clear my mind, and turbo-charge my creativity. Above all – or maybe underneath all – it's the way I connect with the sacred. Moving freely, expressive whilst listening, sexual and spiritual at the same time, dance is my prayer.

Words like 'prayer' and 'spiritual' are loaded with a lot of cultural baggage, so let me say what I mean by them. In my experience, there's a conscious presence within everything that is essentially mysterious to us. We can sense it but we can't grasp it intellectually. This is what I sometimes call Spirit, and being aware of that vast mystery, in touch with it, moved by it, is what I call my spiritual life. Attending to that spiritual life is what I call prayer.

To me, the kind of movement and dance I'm advocating in this book is a spiritual practice, but if those words don't resonate with you, stay with what you find true. I have done my best to write these pages in a way that doesn't require a particular belief about such things. But it's as well for you to know where I'm coming from, so that if my choice of words grate against your own understanding, you can see it for what it is – my perspective, and one that you're under no duress to share.

Becoming a fully integrated human being doesn't just happen. It takes a great deal of loving attention and intelligent, creative training to awaken our astonishing, unique and beautiful brilliance. Most of us didn't get that growing up, but it's never too late, as long as you're still breathing. That is why I have put the practices I have learnt, used, and developed over the last thirty-three years into this book: so that you can become even more truly, deeply, wildly alive.

In this time I've travelled far, and in these pages you'll find some of what I've picked up along the way. You'll learn how to create a movement practice that is both practical and soulful, to explore the vast wilderness that exists within you. You'll pick up some of the best tools I've found and learn how to use them. You'll discover how to practise in ways that work for your unique patterns, hangups and gifts. You'll learn to find your own Pathway Home.

In all this, we'll look at how you can create a space and time that works for your circumstances and preferences – no matter how limited you may believe yourself to be – so that your practice can become something you look forward to and enjoy.

We'll explore the three ways you can practise that will form the backbone of your dance time, and also the vital fourth way that happens in little day-to-day moments. On top of this, we'll breathe into the fifth element that is the core of all meditation practices. I'll give you a key to unlock every obstacle to your practice that you'll ever find, and show you how to turn problems into portals. Crucially, you'll get to explore what your motivation truly is, what it is you're longing for, and how to set foot in that direction using movement as your pathway.

It doesn't matter how many books you read or how often you think about it; there's no substitute for doing it. Taking the first step is the way to begin, taking another is the way to proceed. This book is here to help you do just that: to find your pathway, where you discover that the destination is not a place at all, but a way of going along.

The path *is* home.

How To Use This Book

Life should not be a journey to the grave with the intention of arriving safely in a pretty and well-preserved body, but rather to skid in broadside in a cloud of smoke, thoroughly used up, totally worn out, and loudly proclaiming 'Wow! What a ride!'
— Hunter S. Thompson

You can read this book without trying out any of the material — of course you can. But why would you? Better to go and read a good novel if you're going to just sit there.

No, I would encourage you to get into the mindset of having a go. In fact, how about right now?

Practise: moving with awareness (≥30s)

Allow at least 30s to look up from the page, or even put the book down. Move in some way, whilst being aware of how that feels. Roll your head around your shoulders, or stretch your arms and hands up. Take some deep breaths. Maybe even get up and walk around the room for a moment.

When you stop moving, notice how you feel before you begin reading again.

(Did you do it? No? Go back! Try it out... Give yourself just 30 seconds...)

I'm guessing that, even after moving your body for less than a minute, you feel different. That's what I'm talking about. Don't just read: take steps. As you go through the book, any time you come across a tool that sounds interesting to you, put it into practice and make it your own.

i. Explore freely if you're drawn to do so. It's not essential to read the whole book in order.

ii. Stories from my own journey are in *italics like this.*

iii. Practices you can try for yourself will look like the one above – Practise: moving with awareness (≥30s). Most will have a time guideline, which is the *minimum* you'll need (that's what the ≥ symbol means). You will probably get more out of the practice if you give it more time, particularly for the more emotionally stirring practices; depending on your resilience you may well need longer unless you're very experienced with changing states fast. You may well be best served by allowing some time to pause after a strong practice session before getting on with your day. You'll get a feel for this as you explore the book, and how you might need to adjust my suggested minimum timings.

iv. Be experimental and adventurous! All of the practices in this book can be adapted if you wish, and you may well find that as you engage in a practice, you get a strong sense of needing to change it, in which case I'd encourage you to do so. Try things out and discover what works for you. It's your pathway.

v. If you want to get started without reading my introductions and stories, skip ahead to *Foundations* (Chapter 6). The in-depth practices, techniques and exercises begin in earnest with *Ways to Practise* (Chapter 7). Then you can always return to the earlier sections later if you want a little more background.

vi. I have written this book for people who have some experience with movement and dance already, who wish to ground that in their day-to-day lives. If you don't have that experience, you're still welcome to be here, but I recommend you work through the book chapter by chapter and consider finding a teacher you could study with to strengthen your foundations.

vii. If you do have some experience already, many of the exercises can be used with a modality you're familiar with, such as a ZeroOne evolution, an Open Floor exploration or a 5Rhythms wave. Exercises that are particularly suited to structures in that way have footprints by them but everything can be explored moving freestyle too. It's up to you.

viii. In Appendix I you'll find a list of some of the modalities you can study around the world, most available online as well as live. This book is designed to be a support to all of them.

ix. In British English, we distinguish between *practice* and *practise*. Practice is the noun, a thing that you can engage in, such as yoga, meditation or dance (eg 'My favourite practice is dance'). Practise is the verb, describing the actual doing of it (eg 'Every day I practise dancing'). I'm English, so you'll find both uses in this book.

Writing

Many times here, I'll suggest that you write, so you may want to get a journal specifically to use for your Pathway Home. But whether you use a journal or the back of an old envelope, when you write, do so in the same way that you dance. Let the words flow out, without censoring. As my friend and colleague Lori Saltzman puts it, give your pen to the writer, not the editor. Write like a crazy poet, or an innocent child. Write extra big, or diagonally across the page. Add drawings, blotches, or tear holes in the page. Write passionately, from the heart, from your gut.

If you're a very visual person, any time I suggest you write, you could draw or paint instead. The point is to allow your intelligence to integrate your embodied experience by seeing it through a different lens. It helps bring understanding and open your mind to the extraordinary creative flair that we all carry within us.

Studies investigating the efficacy of various kinds of movement-based work in treating trauma have found that positive effects were significantly stronger and had a longer-lasting impact on their daily lives when the subjects wrote about their experience afterwards. This is because writing makes connections between the two halves of your brain: that which deals in shapes, sensations, feelings and the unknown, and that which deals in words, concepts and the known.

What you go through in movement can be incredibly striking, creating the impression that you'll never forget it. But remember that you're in an altered state of consciousness and, just like a vivid dream, the memory can easily fade after waking. Speaking or writing helps ground it in everyday reality.

And... don't wait for me to suggest picking up a pen. Any time you're stirred up, shut down, full of insight or stumbling in the dark, writing can help.

If you do get a journal, you could use the back pages to make notes, so when something occurs to you to do, you can jot it down for investigation. That could be in the comings and goings of your day, but also, whilst reading you may stumble across one sentence in a paragraph where I'm describing an experience but not specifically giving you an exercise for it, and something inside you jumps up and down, saying 'I need to try that!' Make a note of it. Try it out next time you practise.

Trauma

The practices in this book are powerful. Things will get stirred up, which could include childhood traumas that you didn't even know you had. If you are concerned that you might not be stable or resourced enough to handle what comes up, or if you find yourself feeling out of your depth, please turn to Appendix II before you go any further, and get some support from a trained professional. Exercises that have the potential to be particularly catalytic have this symbol by them: 👀

'I can't . . .'

If you find yourself full of doubts, fears or other reasons not to undertake any of this at all, you are not alone. I've written this book partly because so many people get stuck before even starting. For most of us who went through a conventional education the fear of failure is huge. But as Lao Tzu said, 'Failure is the foundation of success, and the means by which it is achieved.'

So let me encourage you: the times when you struggle, fall, fail, or experience yourself as vulnerable or incompetent will often be opportunities to stumble across your deepest strengths. Striving for something and missing it is fundamental to what makes us human. We reach for the stars – and in the failure to get there we often fall into the underworld and find buried treasure. It is the reaching high that gives us the necessary momentum to fall below the surface.

You will learn the most when it doesn't go so well, and find hidden reserves by going beyond what you know. Any decent practice will sometimes be challenging – it's a good sign if you're hesitant!

You'll find many of these challenges addressed near the end of the book in *Obstacles to Practice* (Chapter 13) but go straight there if you believe 'I can't'.

It's a wild world in there! Don't be too careful – the fullest quality of life as a human is something akin to an art, and true art requires an element of risk. Too much safety will cramp your style, dim your light, and bring a different kind of danger: that of missing out on your deepest power and beauty.

Breathe a little boldness into your bloodstream, and take a step.

Part I: Starting the Journey

1. Why Practise?

If you think you are enlightened, go and spend a week with your family.
— Ram Dass

I'm ridiculously busy today. Non-stop. One of those (thankfully rare) days where there's so much on my to-do list that I skip any kind of morning practice and leap straight for the laptop with a cup of tea as soon as I'm up.

Now it's the afternoon and I've only completed half of the things I intended to tackle. I'm frazzled, and I have to make an important call, the outcome of which matters to me a great deal. It's with someone I look up to, and I'm unsteadily nervous, far from the kind of space I would like to be in.

I give it five minutes. I take this nervous energy and run it through my body, with a whole lot of oxygen. I take one minute to shake and tremble, release the excess fear and frazzle, then I slow it down and pay attention to my balance, using my eyes to orient myself in the room, arms and hands reaching out wide to command the space. Feet spread firm, I practise using that adrenaline as power. Making my breaths gradually slower and deeper, I ground myself as best I can.

When I take the call, I'm still not as calm or strong as I would ideally like to be, but I'm a lot better than I was.

Every moment you devote to dancing through your stuff when you're not being triggered will enable you to be more skillful when you're in a tight spot. I was able to manage my nerves in the situation above so effectively because I've put in time dancing through my fears, including the deep primal terrors that underpin much of the hardwiring of my nervous system.

So that's one answer to the question 'Why practise?' – because you'll be better off if you do. It will make you happier, healthier, and even holier in the sense of being more wholly yourself. Maybe it will even magnetise more sex and money to you. I'm serious: a decent practice such as the kind I'm advocating here will tend to make you truer to yourself, and people who are more thoroughly themselves are generally more attractive and better at what they do in the world. If you don't know your unique gifts, a good practice will tend to help you find them.

You'll find another level of 'why?' if you look at the imprint you make on your circle of friends and family. For me, I can see it particularly in my children: they're less troubled than I was at their age. Some of the stuff I've inherited has been dealt with rather than being passed on. It's as though I'm a lightning conductor, and just like lightning goes to ground, some of the energy of unresolved trauma that came from my forebears has worked its way through my own feet as I danced. It's gone to ground rather than being passed on to my kids. Maybe this sort of inner work is like planting a vineyard – the work is not only for us, but for future generations. OK, you might get to enjoy the sight of something growing and changing – you might even get to eat some grapes – but maybe you'll never get to taste the vintage wine. This is true irrespective of whether you have children of your own or not: your legacy will be implanted in every interaction you have throughout your life.

We are living in wild times, and part of the craziness of what we're living through right now is that much of the way we spend our days – and much of the way we interact with each other – is awfully heady. All those screens! All that thinking, talking and tasking. Learning how to get out of your head and in touch with the natural subterranean wisdom of your body could be a real contribution to the evolutionary leap we need to make. It's urgent.

The third level of 'why?' is harder to put into words. There's something essentially mysterious about being human, about this life we find ourselves in, about the nature of being part of the world. What is it that we're doing here? Why is life the way it is? Who or what are we, deep down? There's something about devoting time to a practice on a regular basis that allows us, if not to answer those questions, then to live them. It enables us to inhabit them, breathe through them, allow them to move through us. This way, our practice becomes valuable in its own right, not because we want a solution to a problem or are looking for a particular outcome, but because it's something we that we love for its own sake. It can become the kind of prayer that is a communion with beauty, mystery, and wonder. It can lend a subtle but profound sense of meaning to your days, and that is priceless.

Having said all this, I have to admit that the primary motivation for me to practise throughout my adult life has been psychological survival. This I have learnt about myself: if I don't devote time to practice on a regular basis, I'm in trouble. Seriously.

Sometimes that practice is a blunt and clumsy emotional release – especially when I've been spending time with my family! Sometimes, a deep stillness might be more the thing. Sometimes movements are minimal, delicate, subtle. I've devoted time to dance on hilltops, in forests, in bedrooms and ballrooms. I've rocked out in silence, with earbuds so as not to wake the kids, and with bone-shaking sound systems along with thousands of other people. I've danced in the middle of the night for hours, and the middle of the day for seconds. All of it has become a lifeline for me, and I don't know how I would have got through without it.

Over time, I've seen patterns in my practice and discovered elements that make it more worthwhile, helping it to make more of a difference in my life.

I reckon you could do the same.

This book is designed to encourage and empower you to give some time to movement and embodiment, giving full attention to your experience, but I'm not talking about an hour a day unless you want to. I'm not necessarily talking about *anything* every day, unless that's what works for you. Choose an amount of time that you can manage, and if that's only three minutes every other day, so be it.

Some of the exercises in this book will need more time than that, but you can start small, and then allow yourself to be drawn towards the more in-depth practices when you're ready. You will soon have the tools to create your own practices too, without needing to refer to any specific exercise here.

Like anything else, the more you put into your practice, the more you'll get out of it. I'd suggest you give it a try daily if you can, but otherwise at regular intervals, and watch the payoff. Go for an amount of time that's small enough to be manageable, then you can increase it if you wish. The key is to make it enjoyable, not stressful. If you over-reach yourself, trying too hard and aiming too far, you'll probably give up, and that's no use to anyone. So relax. Be curious. Approach practising as an experimental and exploratory time, a treasured part of your day. Make it a refuge and a resource, not a burden. Let it be an oasis rather than a task.

As well as any time you give specifically to movement, there are ways of being 'in practice' that can happen throughout your day: at work, with the kids, walking down the street. Embodied presence can become your natural state of being all the time, not just something you do first thing in the morning. It can be a pleasure to remember again and again.

Being a child of 1960s England, the way I have approached 'practice' has mostly been goal-oriented towards self-improvement, starting with the sitting meditation I took on in my late teens. Fuelled by the exotic tales of enlightenment of authors like Alan Watts, Herman Hesse and Ram Dass, I was raring to go, set on achieving my highest potential as a human being. Young man stuff. I wanted badly to climb that mountain.

That was the early 1980s, long enough ago to be weathered by the realities of making my way in the world, but also, that world is now a very different place. The myth we were still living back then was of endless progress and conquest, and whilst a few hopefuls are still clinging to that dream, I don't subscribe to it any more.

It seems evident to me that we're off the edge of the cliff we've been rushing towards for thousands of years. Like a character in a cartoon, our legs are still running but there's no ground underneath us. We're right at that moment of realising we're going down. There's plenty of compulsion to live in denial, hoping that if we keep running fast enough that will stop us from falling, but I reckon it's sheer nonsense.

How can we as individuals stay present, honest, courageous, kind, and response-able even as our collective terror of falling intensifies, with all the attendant frenzy of dissociation, division, and last-ditch decadence?

How can we stay true to our inner compass and instincts when information has become a blur of confusion?

How can we genuinely give something of value to the world we find ourselves in, when the mainstream narrative is still clamouring for more 'stuff' as the solution to all hungers?

How can our practice be more than personal, weaving us closer with the people in our lives and enabling us to glimpse the grace and gifts that come along with falling? How can it soothe the panicky fear of losing what we've relied upon to keep us 'up'?

For me, this is the point of good practice. It helps keep me in touch with my body rather than being carried away by the nagging of my internal dialogue. It helps me to stay emotionally clear, responsive, and warm-hearted. It gives me a toolkit to deal with my dramas, and gives me faith that it's okay to not know much at all. It reminds me again and again, in a visceral way, that life is bigger than me, but that it's within me too – that I am part of life on earth, and the best contribution is to be myself, despite 'myself' being a mystery. And it shows me that all this is best approached with a combination of humility, dedication, and a courageous willingness to fall.

Having spent thousands of years ascending – that is, moving away from the feminine, from the earth, from our bodies – maybe it's time to reconnect. Right now, as the wild beautiful earth is being ravaged and raped at an unprecedented rate, maybe it's time to reconnect with our own personal wilderness, the one that is present inside no matter where we live.

In the body.

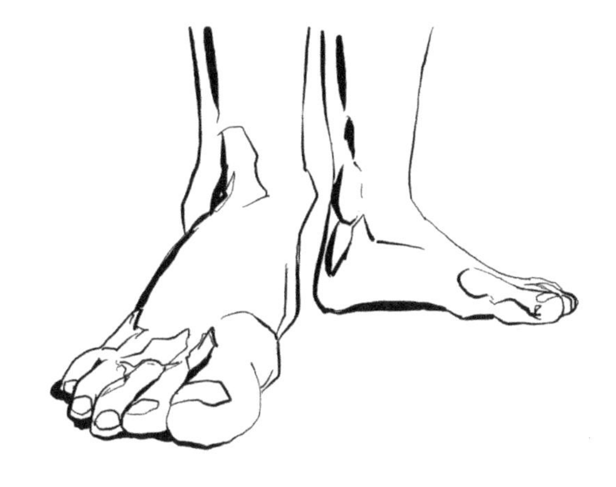

2. Basics

You don't get to the highest levels of the sport without having the basics in order. — Daniel Cormier

Twenty years or so into movement practice, I'm at an advanced-level training with Gabrielle. The room is full of seasoned teachers. She has us working with the most basic level of practice for a whole morning, and it's like drinking cool, clear water. Incredibly refreshing.

Due to the depth of experience in the room, the quality of attention we are able to bring to the moment is electric, but what we are doing is so simple. That's a precious combination, and I'll never forget it.

If you've never been to a dance or movement class anywhere, and you want to give it a go by yourself, then try the simple practices in this chapter. They'll make a good starting point if you're new to movement as a practice.

If you've been doing this for years, they're a vital touchstone. Going back to basics as a movement practitioner is always worthwhile, just as musicians will practise scales throughout their lives.

Breath

Before we go into movement, let me say a bit about breath.

Many embodiment and meditation practices from Eastern countries will advise you to breathe through your nose only, asserting that it is unhealthy to breathe through your mouth. Whether that wisdom originated in very dusty places, or whether it's something else, I do not believe it is the whole truth, especially for emotionally repressed and overly heady Westerners who have been brought up to mistrust their bodies and feelings.

When we have a strong sensory experience, whether pleasurable or painful, the natural instinct of the body is to open the mouth and take a deep breath. It's connection that works both ways: if you breathe through your mouth, you're going to be more strongly connected to your body in a passionate way. If you want to express strong feelings physically, keeping your mouth shut will severely hamper your endeavours. (Try it!)

Breathing only through your nose will tend to make your physiology more self-contained, drawing your attention inwards and calming you down. That's fine, and useful sometimes. But if your intention is to connect more strongly to your feelings and sexual energy, to be more spontaneous and free rather than controlled and heady, more expressive and in vibrant relationship to the world around you, then relax that jaw and let your breath come through your mouth.

Let's try a few different ways of using your breath to get the sense of what a powerful tool it can be.

Practise: Activation Breath (1m)

This will tend to intensify your experience of your feelings:
Take a few breaths with your mouth relaxed and open.
Try breathing deeper and fuller.
Notice what changes in your body.

Practise: Releasing Breath (1m)

This will tend to take whatever energy is activated in you and allow it to release. Breathe in through your nose, then gently let the exhale come out of your mouth, taking even longer than the inhale. Notice the last wisps of breath as they come out.

Variation: During the inhale, breathing into your belly before your chest will allow your feelings to release and settle more quickly. Place a hand on your belly to help you feel it expanding with your inhale through the nose, then gently let the exhale come out of your mouth, taking even longer than the inhale. Notice the last wisps of breath as they come out.

Variation: Holding your breath for a moment before you exhale will deepen the sense of release.

Variation: Allowing a sigh to come with the exhale will deepen the sense of release.
Variation: Enjoying a slight pause before you inhale will deepen a sense of settled calm.

Practise: Calming Breath (≥1m)

Relax your face, including the jaw, but place the tip of your tongue gently on the roof of your mouth just behind your front teeth. Breathe through your nose, allowing whatever rhythm comes completely naturally. Scan through your body, feeling the pull of gravity on every part of you and dropping into the sense of relaxed physicality. Watch the breath come and go.

Aaahhhhh... So good... Nothing to be done.

I cannot overstate how vital your relationship with your breath is. Making it a conscious part of your movement practice is possibly the single most effective thing you can do in terms of the ratio of effort to what you get in return. It's immediate: one conscious breath changes everything, and no matter how experienced you are, this back-to-basics step is forever.

Simple Movement Practices

So, to movement. There are many ways to start a session, and different ones will appeal to you on different days.

Here are three simple practices to start you off:

1. Practise: Feet First (≥5m)

Your feet are the most grounded part of you. They're the one part of you that your monkey mind cannot reach with its wily ways — feet stay completely ordinary. If you have a tendency towards emotional dramas like I do, that's priceless. Giving attention to the way your feet move is a great way to get present, down to earth and real.

i) With bare feet or only socks, stand with your feet shoulder-width apart and your knees softened so you have the sensation of sitting gently and stably in the bowl of your hips. Notice the weight of your body coming down through your hips, legs, ankles and feet into the floor, feeling for a supple solidity in the whole arrangement.

ii) Wriggling your toes, squirming the whole of each foot around, explore the way they feel on the floor, and how much movement they have in them even when you're not walking. Bones, muscles and more... what sensations do you have?

iii) Begin to experiment with lifting your feet, putting them in different places, moving around the room, letting them go in all directions — backwards, forwards, side to side, round and round on the spot. Explore creative footsteps. Hop, skip, jump, slide — go slow, fast, big, small, light, heavy, carefully, boldly.

iv) If you're new to this, consider stopping there after a few minutes. Pause, breathe, feel. Notice how you're doing — what's going on in your body? If you feel up for going further then start again, and this time, rather than pausing, keep going to the next steps.

v) Once your feet are in gear and you're moving around the room, begin to allow the rest of your body to follow their lead. How can you allow everything to be in dynamic relationship with your feet? Experiment! Can you engage your hips with the rhythm of your feet? Can you let the weight of your head drop and be part of your body? Can you allow your arms and hands to join in?

vi) Let your breath come and go freely and allow whatever emerges through the rest of your body as you follow your feet. It's OK to be clunky, funky, or fierce. If it feels weird, be curious and stay with it. If it's difficult, struggle valiantly. If it's fun, light up with everything you have.

vii) Let this run its course for as long as feels 'right', whether that's for one minute or half an hour. Pay attention to how you feel in your body, and trust your impulses.

Take time to be with the aftermath of your movement. Be still, staying present with your body. Can you sense the need for anything else to complete your experience? To go outside and greet the day? Journal what you found? Call your best friend? Value this time that comes after the movement as an integral part of your practice. Be open to knowing, seeing, feeling.

2. Practise: Inspired (≥3m)

Focusing on your breath is the bread and butter of most meditation practices, and you can take it to a whole new level by learning to embody the breath and move with it. Delicious.

i) Become still and notice your breath. Be conscious of what feels right to you in this moment and either allow your breath through your mouth or just the nose. Go inside, closing your eyes if you wish, or just softening your gaze. Where do your hands want to be? Would it feel good to place one hand on your belly, the other on your heart?

ii) Notice the subtle movement that's already happening from your breath. If you pay close attention, you may be able to sense that your whole body is involved.

iii) Let that subtle movement be your inspiration. Start with it and let it grow. Notice how your body wants to move if you stay aware of your breath.

iv) Stay aware of what breathing style feels right to you, through the mouth or nose, and either let it change naturally or consciously experiment with changing it.

v) There may be many times when you pause, resting within an awareness of what's going on in your body. When the urge comes to move again, allow that. There's no rush, and nothing to achieve. Listen for the intimacy of the relationship between body and breath, and let it move you.

Take time to be with the aftermath of your movement. Be still, staying present with your body. Can you sense the need for anything else to complete your experience? To go outside and greet the day? Journal what you found? Call your best friend? Value this time that comes after the movement as an integral part of your practice. Be open to knowing, seeing, feeling.

3. Practise: Inside Out (1-5m)

I find this practice incredibly useful if I'm triggered in some way and don't have much time to process what's going on. It's a fast-track pathway to relative clarity, allowing whatever state you're in to be thoroughly experienced, integrated with insights, and then to change.

However, you can also try it when feeling more or less neutral emotionally, and in fact, I would recommend you do so, especially if you're new to this kind of practice. At least once or twice, try out the whole sequence when you're feeling relatively balanced and grounded. Then, when you're more triggered in some way, you have the tool and can use it to release your feelings and change state.

i) Allow your body to take a shape. There's no right or wrong, just experiment. If you're in a strong emotional state then let the shape reflect that, embodying whatever it is you're feeling. You can do this many times, so you get used to trying out different shapes to start with. Involve your whole body, not just your arms and hands. As you gain experience, you can go further and try out more unusual shapes, with more and more departure from straight-up-and-normal. Remember: you are strange. We all are! Let the unique quality of the moment come through your body, allowing you to get a sense of yourself physically.

ii) Breathe deeply through your mouth as well as your nose, which will help you to connect with the feeling tone of your shape, the story of it.

iii) Now you're going to let that shape move in a simple physical repetition, in sync with your breath. Inhale into the original shape, exhale out to another one. Back and forth, back and forth, allowing the feeling quality of the moment to express itself through your movement.

iv) Exaggerate the movements bigger and faster, with more breath. Be willing to get passionate, even to the extent that the feeling and the movement may take over with a life of their own.

v) Bit by bit, allow the movements and breath to get more gentle and relaxed, slowing down over time. Don't rush this slowdown — even if you feel like collapsing, tenderly stay with it. If you sense your body wanting the movements and the shapes to change, then go with that.

vi) Even as you come to a natural end or pause point, stay present with your body, breath, and felt-sense of what's going on inside you. You may find yourself suddenly tearful or laughing. You may need to fall to the floor or open the window for fresh air. Trust your impulses.

vii) Listen in to your body with an open mind. Is there anything it's saying to you?

Awareness and Attention

Awareness is a 'field' of consciousness, open to everything that's happening, and has a quality of *being*.

Attention is consciousness that's focused upon something specific, to the exclusion of everything else, and has a quality of *doing*.

You will need both for any good-quality movement work. Being aware will enable you to stay open to learning in ways you don't expect, noticing when something new comes up or needs to change. Choosing where to put your attention will enable you to wield your consciousness as a tool for directing energy, enabling you to practise and learn in alignment with your intentions.

Let's explore each.

Practise: Awareness (≥5m)

i) Stand still to begin with. Drop into your body, softening your knees a little, loosening your shoulders and allowing your belly to be what it is. Let your face relax, as though you're letting a mask fall off. Take a deep breath and let it go.

ii) Gently, as though you're seeing an invisible mist, or listening to a silence, become aware of your awareness. Settling within yourself, opening to the experience of being aware. Maybe it can feel like resting as awareness.

iii) Once you feel some stability in that experience, you can allow movements to come. Start small at first, gradually expanding your range, and simply allow the sense of resting as awareness to include whatever movement is happening.

iv) If you lose the sense of resting as awareness, try going back to being still, or letting the movements get smaller again. Experiment with how far you can go into movement — how big, how fast — whilst still having a sense of being the field of awareness that permeates through and even around your whole body.

Practise: Attention (≥10m)

i) Scan through your body, listening for one part of you that is calling for your attention. There's no right or wrong: you'll learn something whatever you choose, so have faith in your first impulse. Maybe it's a place that's hurting or stiff, maybe you feel unusually energised there, or maybe you're just intuitively drawn to it. It could be one tiny spot like your right thumb, or a large area such as your left side.

ii) Placing your attention there, let your breath deepen. Imagine your breath going especially to that area and allow it to begin moving. Be curious, finding out how it's able to move, sensing how it *wants* to move.

iii) Once you've got the feel of it, let that one part of you lead the rest of your body until everything else is following. Give yourself to it wholeheartedly. If you find yourself feeling emotional, pour those feelings through your movement too.

iv) Let it take you on a journey, following through until you're done.

v) Allow some time for being still, so the whole experience can settle within you.

vi) Bonus: get pen and paper and let that part of your body write. Write in the style of that part of you (does it write tiny or big, messy or neat?) without it needing to make logical sense.

Calming, Grounding, Resting

The world was a very different place when I started using movement as a practice. In the late '80s and '90s, I had a need to blow the lid off, let stuff out and go wild that was personal to me, but it was in tune with the collective zeitgeist as well. We danced 'til we dropped, for days and days, with never a thought for calming down, and we loved it.

Times have changed. Many people's nervous systems are seriously and chronically challenged right now, which means that rather than going wild, we often have a deep need to calm down, get grounded and rest. In my opinion, there are three reasons for this:

- We're facing emergencies on a scale to make the most optimistic of us baulk. We cannot witness the sixth great extinction of our planet, along with the breakdown of so many human parameters of well-being, whilst staying 'just fine'. The word 'stressful' is hopelessly inadequate.

- Every time a piece of new information enters your awareness, even if it's 'positive' news, your nervous system gets activated in much the same way as it does when something scary or exciting happens. Even a text message or email falls into this category. Make that 'bad news' and the level of activation is higher still. Most of us are constantly flooded with new information like this, from dozens of sources. Stressful.

- Because our devices such as phones and computers respond to our commands with something that seems like intelligence, our nervous system tends to treat them like a relational partner. We get a 'hit' of relational experience every time we do anything with them. Then factor in that we're wired for resonance: one of the vital aspects of our nature as humans is to seek common ground and mirror each other. Now look how fast computers react to a click, and try to mirror that. Your nervous system tries instinctively to respond similarly quickly in order to be in resonance with your electronic friend. More stress.

All of this means we are chronically and severely stressed in ways that we haven't evolved to deal with. It's too much. You may not even realise how overdriven you are, but riding roughshod over your need to rest is not a good idea.

Here are some ways you can calm down, which I'd recommend you practise when you're feeling okay so that you are already skilled in them when you need them most.

Practise: calming down (≥1m each)

As with all these simple methods, don't just do them in a functional way. Take time enough that you can *feel from the inside* what is going on within you. Do one or two, pausing after each to notice what's going on for you. Don't do them all one after another; that's just more of the 'too much' we need calming down from.

i) Walk around your space with long, relaxed strides, looking around you. Gradually walk slower and slower until you naturally come to a stop. Pause, enjoying the stillness.

ii) Focus your eyes on a place or object in the room, taking time to look properly at what you're seeing. You could reach out and touch it, feeling its texture and shape.

iii) Sitting comfortably, wrap your arms around yourself, tenderly. Hug yourself soothingly. You could also try this rocking slowly and gently from side to side or front to back.

iv) Stand with your feet shoulder-width apart, knees slightly bent. Feel your weight, the steady, gentle pull of gravity on your whole body. Relax into that.

v) Stand with your feet shoulder-width apart, knees slightly bent, and shift your weight slowly from one foot to the other. Go from one side with a long inhale to the other side with a long exhale. You could do this with your arms relaxed by your sides, or wrapped around yourself in a warm hug.

vi) Gently place one hand on your belly and one on your heart. Experiment with which feels best — left hand on belly, right hand on heart, or the other way round? Feel what it's like to embrace and protect your vulnerability.

vii) Let your arms and hands lift up as you inhale, and down as you exhale. Experiment with how big to make the movements: what feels healthy?

viii) Inhale through the nose and exhale slowly through the mouth with a soft sigh.

ix) Breathe intentionally into your belly more than your chest. Allow the exhale as a letting go, a relaxation. This can help you settle when you're intensely emotional.

x) Hold your belly tenderly with your left hand whilst making slow, soothing circles around the centre of your chest with your right hand, moving clockwise (down on the left of your chest, up on the right).

xi) Gently hold one of your thumbs wrapped in the fingers of the other hand. After a while, switch hands.

xii) Get a great big cushion or pillow and hug it to your body. You could do this standing, sitting or lying down. Hold onto it, feeling the need for comfort and feeling the need being met.

xiii) Lie down or sit comfortably and notice the pull of gravity on your body, breathing naturally and easily.

xiv) Rest. Just rest. That's all. Be comfortable. If you fall asleep, great.

When you're learning, taking in new information or going through any kind of change, the process requires that you rest. Part of the learning process only happens when you rest. It doesn't complete otherwise. Moving straight onto the next thing can be an addiction, keeping you hooked on the activated state of 'new'. This compulsion ensures that you never integrate anything thoroughly, creating a discomfort that has you reaching for yet another stimulus when what you actually need is to calm down and rest. This addiction is a main runner for so many people leading western lifestyles now. Me too – gosh, it's hard to stop. And, it's so good to stop.

Basics Endnotes

If you are new to all this, practise these basics and then enjoy exploring the rest of this book, but I highly recommend you don't stop here. Home practice is a robust and enlightening part of your toolkit, but it's also incredibly valuable to get yourself to classes or workshops with high-quality teachers and have the experience of dancing with a group.

The most effective mix, if you really want to go for it full-on and have movement as a stonkingly powerful tool for awakening, healing and well-being, is some home practice most days, an evening class most weeks, and a weekend or longer workshop a few times a year. Rocket fuel. Seriously.

See Appendix I for suggestions of modalities you could try, and find yourself a teacher you can learn from. Get some recommendations, read up about them, try out something they're offering online so you can get a sense of their teaching style. Go to a live event, but if it doesn't feel right in your body to be there, walk away and try something or someone else.

3. Why Practise At Home?

I am not going anywhere; I am only on my way.
— Siddhartha, Hermann Hesse

As a young boy, I had the good fortune to live in Tanzania for a couple of years, and I struck up a relationship with the black man who cleaned and cooked for us, which is what the deal was with white people living there in those days. He had something that my parents did not, and the land had something that England did not. I liked him, and I liked Africa, both of them touching a latent knowledge in my bones, like a tuning fork.

Fast forward to the late '80s, and day two of an 'Encounter Group'. After a gruelling Saturday that had gone on well after midnight, we were woken early to do a 'Dynamic Meditation' practice before breakfast. It involved a lot of chaotic breathing, moving, shouting and sweating, all of which was undertaken blindfolded. After some time feeling weird and ungainly, I suddenly got into it. I felt that spirit of Africa surge through my blood, all the way from my childhood. Silently thanking the man who had seen through me as a boy, I was able to pour myself into this wild and cathartic dance that reminded me of something ancient, something bigger than me, something deeper than my own culture. I was coming home, to a strange land.

If you've fallen in love with dance and movement, you probably did so in a group, led by someone playing powerful music, in a big open space. You may have had encounters with other dancers that caused you to become as intimate as old friends or lovers without even knowing their names, let alone what they do for a living. If it was a class, you probably danced for a couple of hours straight; if it was a longer workshop you might have dived in deep for days.

But have you ever experimented alone in your living room, full of the business and busyness of your daily life, for five, ten or twenty minutes? Even without any music? Have you tried to incorporate dance into your routine in those ways, regularly, for a few weeks? At first glance, this type of movement might sound like second-best compared with a strong group experience, but there are strengths and subtleties to be found in practising at home.

Entering into movement on your own, where you decide the timing, the soundscape and the structure, will bring you into a quality of relationship with your practice that you cannot find any other way.

Nowadays, you can find movement classes in most big cities across the western world. Most of the pioneers of such practices no longer walk the earth, but the seeds they planted have blossomed into an incredibly rich variety of offerings, with hundreds of styles available.

It was very different when I first found Osho's dynamic meditations and Gabrielle's 5Rhythms in the late 1980s. They were esoteric experiences, found in occasional weekend workshops. I had spent my late teens and early twenties sitting in meditation for an hour a day, so when I discovered dance as a practice, it felt natural to take the same everyday approach. There were no regular classes anywhere, so I practised wherever I happened to be. I was living in a van at that point, literally on the road, so my practice spaces were a mix of forests, mountainsides, or friends' spare rooms.

That foundation of regular home practice has given me a relationship with movement that doesn't depend on anyone or anything, and I treasure it. I've used it in countless crises, stuck with it through boredom, wrestled with long phases of losing my way and wondering what the hell I'm doing. It is the stable ground – the rocket fuel – that enables me to show up and participate in my family and the world, far more generously and creatively than I could without it.

So many of the people who come to work with me don't have that. They believe that they need a teacher or a group or music in order to practise, and I ache for them.

Is that you? Do you know what you're missing?

It's been natural for me to continue having embodiment as part of my life, and it's my preferred way to start the day. Sometimes it's dramatic, like a day in the woods where I once fought the 'nice guy' role I was brought up to play – I shouted, stamped and flung myself around, smashing up dead branches, giving a lifetime of repressed anger a clear pathway through my body until I was empowered, free, and vibrantly alive. Other days it's quite ordinary. Sometimes it's clearly 'dance', other times it's more meditative, even still. Often it feels vital for my wellbeing. Usually, the times when I don't feel like practising are the most valuable of all.

I'm pretty flexible with my daily practice, mixing up different ways to be 'in attendance'. That includes elements of seated meditation, walking in the woods, sitting with a candle mumbling to the gods, or doing yoga stretches. The days I have more than an hour feel abundant, but it could be as little as a few minutes. Micro-practices pepper my days, and often I use some kind of embodiment tool for literally a few seconds. Occasionally I will miss a day, but that is rare, and it leaves me feeling barren, incomplete, and subtly frustrated. I have done some kind of daily practice for forty years now, and I imagine I will do so until I drop.

This might seem like a lot of discipline, and I guess it is, but not in the sense of exerting willpower over some other errant parts of me. That never works for long. No, it's more like a mix of devotion and desperation.

4. Discipline, Devotion and Desperation

… I am a strange fan of monastic discipline. In clear minded moments I might find this as bracing and inspiring as I do a winter storm. I love storms, the wilder the better. They're just not matters of opinion. They're Gods. Storms are a non-negotiable notice about who and what is in charge of the proceedings. Apprentices to limits: That's what we could become. — Stephen Jenkinson

I'm strung out. It's been a long day and I'm exhausted, though not physically. I've spent the whole day with my hands on a keyboard or mouse, scrutinising screens or talking on the phone. Postponing the urge to crack open a beer, I decide to give ten minutes to practice.

Sensing into the jittery head-spinning multi-tasking mix of control and speed that I've been dabbling in all day, I give it all to my body, shaking all over, almost violently, for a

few minutes. Then I sit quietly and pay attention to my breath and body. Immediately, I gratefully fall into, expand into, become, a sense of spaciousness with no edges, a silence without place. It's such a pleasure. Such a relief.

The timer goes too soon, and I sit there a little longer. The jittery exhaustion is still there, but not nearly so bad. I go for the beer, but with less compulsion. I drink it more slowly than I would have done, wondering if a really 'good' practitioner would be drinking herbal tea.

Discipline is a word that's become commonly associated with controlling and even oppressing children, including inner ones. However, the original root of the word is the same as for 'disciple', which is a whole different thing. Discipleship is about love and learning, not control. It can be a kind of devotion, or longing.

Love of learning has been the heart of my path and my saving grace. Since I was a boy, in truth, I have been a pilgrim, a disciple, devoted to – how to say it? – learning to have a flesh-and-blood experience of the Vast Mystery that IS. By this I mean the divine, although none of the words we use for it feel entirely satisfying to me.

Many of my days though, I've felt too far away from that love of the Mystery to have much of a sense of connection with it. At those times, devotion becomes more like a longing, or yearning, but that's enough to get me to practise. It's not about willpower so much as remembering what I love and choosing to give it time.

Then there's the desperation. My beginning years were horrifying enough to leave gaping wounds – traumas operating way below my conscious awareness. I had no recall of that as I vaguely passed the 'Adult' milestone, but I knew I was tortured deep inside. In desperation to get out of hell, I turned to spiritual and shamanic practices, therapy, bodywork, and a lot of self-help books. Slowly, slowly, I developed the resilience to be with the pain that was driving me, to find compassion for myself in there, and heal.

So what about you? What are you desperate for? Do you dare let yourself feel that need? What are you devoted to, deep down? Have you found it?

If you haven't, can you feel the longing?

The practice below could bring up strong feelings. It did with me when I last tried it, I found myself going through fear and fury before I came to a gritty determination that felt good, healthy and true. If it's something like that for you, plunge yourself into the experience. Let your emotional energy move. Let it be e(nergy)-in-motion. Let it pull you far beyond your normal dance shapes, into the wilderness of your unknown selves. Stay with the process until you're done.

Practise: Calling (≥10m)

Get pen and paper ready. (No, your phone won't work for this kind of writing.)

Let your feet carry you around your space with the intention of listening for your motivation. Step in all directions, moving forwards, backwards, side to side, turning around on the spot. Travel at your own pace, with big or small steps. If you sense your body needing to stretch, shake, or stamp, go for it.

Add your voice — as you move around the room, following your feet wherever they take you — whisper, ask, or shout out loud 'What's calling me?' Ask again and again, not grasping for answers but rather letting the question live through your whole being, through your body, breath, and voice.

If you dance this question, letting it really *get* to you, what comes up? How do you feel? Can you let those feelings become part of your dance? If there's a lost-ness, or a not-knowing, or a desire in the mix, how does that shape you?

Once you have the sense that you're totally infused with this question, ask yourself what more accurately fits your feeling right now: desperation, longing, or devotion? Choose one, and write down the words 'I am desperate for...' or 'I am longing for...' or 'I am devoted to...' and then keep writing. Don't censor or edit. Just let the words pour out.

Now read back what came. Let the truth of it sink in without any imperative to act on it yet. Just feel it.

That's your motivation, right there. Maybe you'll distill what you've written to a single sentence and write it on a postcard that you send yourself, or pin on the fridge. Maybe you'll do that exercise again in a few days' time.

For me, it was always clear that what motivated me was a mix of all three. It was such an imperative – such a strong calling – that I didn't struggle with motivation until many years later. Decades into my long relationship with dance, I began to falter and had to dig deeper, asking myself whether this is actually my thing any more. I questioned what I was looking for, what effect I was having on myself and my world by spending my time in movement, an enquiry that opened up my practice in a whole new way.

I know that lack of motivation is high on the list of why people might not get round to a practice session. If that's so for you, it might help to listen deeply inside yourself in this way, and sense into what it is you truly desire.

When Gabrielle asked me, 'Do you have the discipline to be a free spirit?', I was determined the answer would be a 'Yes!'

How about you?

5. Your Pathway

Return to the beginning. Enter by form. Clean your dojo. As you have every day, tie on the white belt and empty your cup. Pick up your guitar, tune, then play. — Philip Toshio Sudo

I'm just home from a two-week intensive with Gabrielle Roth, and I have the distinct impression that my entire world, not to mention sense of self, has shattered. I'm not who I was.

At sea, I fall back on the most reliable thing I have: my practice. Beginning to move, tears fall at the relief of this intimate, stable, familiar touchstone, so different from the wildfire of a workshop with Gabrielle alongside a hundred other burning souls. Home again. I integrate all that electricity into everyday reality, grounding myself one step at a time. Day after day, slowly, slowly, I'm home again.

It may be that you have come to this book without any experience of movement practice as part of a group. If so, welcome! You may be in the same boat as I was when I began, armed with a book and a whole heap of enthusiasm and curiosity.

If, however, you've been going to classes or workshops for some time already, there are good reasons to take your practice into your own hands, to learn how to travel solo and take time to move at home, on the beach, or in the forest. There are strengths and gifts you won't find in a class or workshop with someone else holding the space for you, no matter how much time you spend there.

- *Empowerment*: Practising alone, you'll find your own authority — you become the author of your experience. You'll have to establish your unique relationship with movement and make it your own. You set the space, choose the time. You source the music or choose the silence. You decide what steps to take. No one else is accountable, and there is nothing like it.
- *Flexibility*: It's so natural to us to fall into resonance with each other that when you're participating in a group, it takes some effort to do anything other than swim along with the collective current (or helplessly react against it if you're locked into rebel or outsider mode). You're dealing with more than your own path and presence, which can make it difficult to focus on specific issues you may have. On your own, you can flow with the ups and downs of your energy much more freely, and even create whole practice sessions precisely designed to explore what's up in your world rather than following anyone else's agenda.
- *Subtlety*: Groups create strong energy fields. I'll never forget walking into a room at the end of a weekend workshop I had not been part of. The atmosphere was so thick I could have taken a bite out of it. I love that kind of intensity, but for some stages of inner work it can be completely overwhelming, impossible to be part of without some degree of dissociation or overriding of one's sensitivity. Even if being in groups is no problem for you, there's a fine-drawn quality of experience you can find only in solo practice. Some things happen only when we attend to that which is small, quiet and subtle.
- *Integrating Change*: There is no question that you can have profound experiences moving with a group of other practitioners while someone holds the space skilfully — and the longer you're at it, the deeper you'll go. Workshops can be life changing. But it's common to have a significant backlash after that kind of transformative journey — as though your psyche was attached by elastic to its habitual ways of being. One way of looking at this is that you didn't have the ground within your daily life to sustain and stabilise such a depth of change. A regular home practice will give you more of that grounded stability. If you have a strong practice on your own, you can fly further and higher in a workshop, and you'll have somewhere to land once you return home. That's when you need a

clear, stable baseline, and it's no good trying to create it overnight when you need it. You have to practise when you don't need it, then it'll be there for you, ready. When you come home somewhat destabilised and ungrounded, with turbulent energy and feelings that can be anything from ecstatic to dissociated, you will integrate more smoothly if you can fall back on a familiar practice that anchors that new self within your daily life.

- *Ordinariness*: getting into seriously altered states of consciousness can be fun, and it's often a strong feature of practising movement in groups, but having a practice that has an ordinary quality to it is tremendously valuable too. It may not be so glamorous to our inner adolescent, but something quiet grows over time when we show up regularly for ourselves, no matter what the weather. I think of it as a long-term relationship. Day by day, year by year, a trust develops that I'm in it for the duration, that I don't have to create drama or excitement to get my own attention. I'll be there anyway. When love can be ordinary, we can breathe a sigh of relief and relax into it.

These are my top reasons for practising at home, but there's a bonus one: if you're lucky enough to have a partner who likes to dance too, then you can practise with them, no holds barred. This is more difficult when you're with a group, where you would probably want to limit how far you go with each other, whether fighting or fucking. For Maria-Carin and me, being able to dance together is anything between a joy and couple-survival. Ways to approach this might be another book in itself, but you could have a go at any of the exercises in this book with your beloved (or adapt them to suit, or create your own) and share with each other what your experience was.

Doubt, and Small Moves

For a long time I've had the urge to write, and I always thought I'd publish a book or two one day. 'Book!' seemed like an awfully big task though, and several attempts at starting something went nowhere, leaving me feeling overwhelmed and inadequate. I repeatedly gave up after a few pages. I have a sad folder on an external hard drive that I can't quite bear to delete, like a small graveyard for these miscarriages of creativity.

Then a friend suggested I just start writing a blog on my website, to get in the swing of things with something smaller. Great idea. This book came quite easily after a few years of practising in that way.

Despite seeing how useful, challenging and enjoyable it could be to have a movement practice at home, you might doubt your ability to show up for yourself.

If so, you may want to skip straight to the section on stumbling blocks towards the end of the book: *Obstacles to Practice* (Chapter 13). There, you'll find ways to take obstacles into your practice, which is far more interesting and fruitful than attempting to overcome them.

For now though, let me say this:

Doubts often come when we set ourselves goals that are too high.

For example, how long do you think you should practise for? Does something change if you let go of that 'should' and instead ask yourself, 'What amount of practise would I feel excited about?'

One minute of practice is a lot more than none.

Three minutes is *much* more than one.

And so on.

If you get to a regular twenty minutes, you could be into life-changing territory, especially if you use the Focus and Give practice modes outlined in this book. But I'd strongly suggest you don't even look that far ahead. There are huge benefits to be had with short practice sessions, especially if you go there regularly. One minute every day for a month, if you haven't done that before, will change your relationship with your body and your movement practice. I bet you. (In fact, if you try it and I'm wrong, let me know and you can have a refund on this book.)

What I'm saying is:

START SMALL

Really small ...

If you start small, it's manageable, and you can experience success over and over again. Success feels good, which will make the whole prospect feel much more attractive. You wouldn't start a jogging practice by trying to run ten miles a day. At least, I hope not! You'd hurt yourself, feel like a failure, and would probably never make it as far as day two. Indeed, running only half a mile each day might be just right for you, and it would keep you far healthier than nothing.

If you start with something you can do easily and increase it a tiny bit as it feels right until you're at a level that feels good, you'll establish a groove that will soon come naturally to you. After a while you'll miss it when you don't show up, like you might miss a morning coffee.

This is far more effective than the 'should' program. After all, aren't you reading this book because of something you love, or are longing for?

Focus on the love, or the longing.

Don't you have some curiosity about
what might become of you if...?

Follow that question mark.

One step at a time.

Small moves.

How about one right now?

Practise: taking a step (≥1m)

Stand, and look around the room. Check in with your body — what can you sense? Are you leaning forward, or holding back? Hedging your bets over to one side perhaps?

Notice your breathing. Do you need to take a deeper breath right now? How do you feel, to be doing a simple embodiment practice, on your own, with nobody else around?

When you're ready: slowly, deliberately, take one step and stand in the new place.

Stay aware of how you feel in your body the whole time.

That's it! Done. Something subtle will have changed. Can you feel it?

You cannot take a single step without moving the world. Take that one step, and consider your practice done for now. Notice how it feels to treasure small moves, valuing the fact that you took a step.

6. Foundations

If you don't have a spiritual practice when times are good,
you can't expect to suddenly develop one during a moment of crisis.
— Douglas Coupland

I haven't set a timer, but chaotically dive into morning practice, already under pressure from the day's to-do list. I have no idea how long I'm going to practise for, but begin moving anyway, with the vague intention of allowing the frustrated mass of feelings coursing through me to get some airtime.

I move for a few moments, then get irritated by a pile of papers that's not where it should be. Then I need a drink of water. I start moving again but feel tired and realise my legs need to stretch before I can do anything else. Before I've even finished stretching, the messy emotional state that drove me to the floor ten minutes ago resurfaces, and I'm on my feet again. I'm thrashing around haphazardly, releasing something, my thinking mind constantly nagging me about how ineffective I am being.

I finally make a decision: stop. Just stop and feel. I can just about discern that underneath the angry stuff, I'm hurting. I stay with that awhile, softening, breathing a little easier.

I walk into the day a little more whole, grounded and relaxed. Practice took fifteen minutes. If I'd set a timer for 15 right at the start, I probably would have had a much clearer time, and gone further.

My practice becomes more effective if I set the stage with some clear boundaries. I don't always do this — sometimes I'm fine with being very informal and relaxed — but often my practice will suffer if I'm not clear.

I'm easily distracted. The main triggers for me are: the future (like, what I am supposed to be doing in an hour's time) and little things I notice in my space that need dealing with (such as a mug that's been left on the desk). In addition, those triggers will get to me much more easily if I'm fuzzy about my intention for the session.

Attending to these three simple components helps me to create good solid ground, forming a strong triangle to support my practice session:

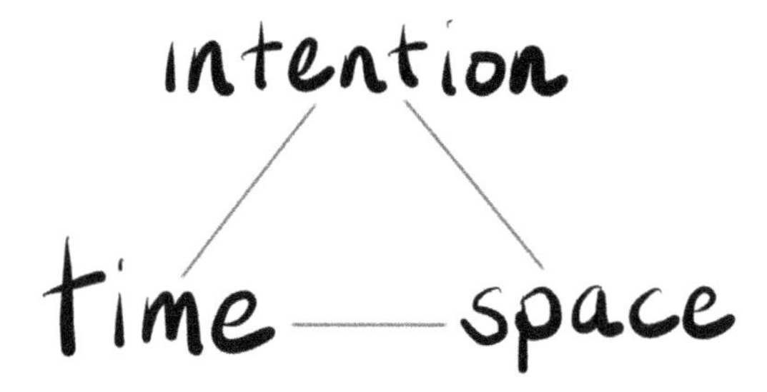

It helps me to stay present and give everything to the moment if I set a timer, tidy up the room a bit, and get clear about my intentions.

Attending to boundaries gives us a sense of drawing a circle around ourselves so that, as we step in, there're a clearer and more sacred quality to it, enabling us to open and engage more deeply in the process.

What are your distractions? How could you set things up to minimise them?

Time

The first thing you'll need in developing a daily practice is time. This is not always easy to find in our over-driven, neo-protestant, rat-race culture. But know this: you don't need much to make a valuable contribution to your day. Even one minute will make a difference. Even one deep breath will!

So be realistic and choose an amount of time you can manage, starting small. Seriously – it is far better to practise for three minutes and feel good about it than put pressure on yourself to find half an hour a day which then becomes a stress or a burden. That's a sure road to giving up.

Little and often will go further than occasional big chunks: 3 minutes a day for a month will serve you far better than a one-off 90-minute session.

Time gives you a straightforward boundary. If you're using music, that will frame your practice, but otherwise, set a timer and enjoy the sense of completion when the bell goes.

A timer that can be set to go off multiple times is great for days when you want to go through several sections of practice. I have one that uses the sound of a Tibetan singing bowl, which is a huge improvement on the standard electronic beeps most phones have.

Practise: timing (1 - 7m)

Decide on an amount of time to practise that's 7 minutes or less. What amount of time would you feel excited or curious about?

Set a timer, press go, and then move freestyle until the time is up.

Now be still for a moment, giving yourself a chance to feel what's happened and where you've landed.

Space

As well as time, you'll need space. For some years, I was lucky enough to have a dedicated room at home for movement practice. I loved that, but it's not essential. Where I live now, our living room is our main practice space. It's not huge, and it's got plenty of distractions because it's used for other things, but it's enough.

Many days I'll head out to a quiet spot in the park around the corner for morning practice, or cycle over to nearby woods or the top of a hill for sunrise, and move there. I've often danced in a spare bedroom when visiting friends. The award for my making-the-most-of-what's-available practice space would have to go to an aeroplane bathroom. Long haul flights are much relieved by a bit of movement, and I'm too private to do that in the aisles. I don't mind stretching or sitting in meditation whilst being watched, but when I dance, my soul becomes visible. I'm choosy about who gets to see that, and when.

Whatever space I do have, it helps to create a sense of clarity if I tidy up a bit, get rid of any clutter and light a candle. I switch off the phone and close the door, maybe the curtains too.

Practise: clear space (≥3m)

Move for a few minutes in your space without preparing it in any way. Leave the phone switched on.

Now turn the phone off, make your space a bit clearer and more dedicated to your practice.

Move again for a few minutes and feel the difference.

Intention

Whether you're conscious of it or not, you have an intention for everything you do, and that includes your practice. It will make your movement experience more effective if you get clear about what your intention is before you start.

Intention is not something you make up in your head, but more like something you listen for in your body. It's already there. If you get quiet enough, you'll sense it.

Practise: getting clear about your intention (≥10m)

Clear your space and decide on an amount of time that you're going to practise.

Next, by way of further preparation, be quiet, still, and turn your attention inwards. Listen for the sense of your intention that's already there. Where do you sense it is in your body? What does it feel like? Is it pushing forwards, or receptive and open? Is there any emotional quality around it?

(If you are too busy or chaotic inside yourself to get any clear sense of intention, here's a way to get clearer: move like crazy, in the most busy and chaotic way you can manage for two minutes. Go for it! Now become still, and listen.)

How might you articulate this sense of intention in words? Can you get that down to the essence, so that it's only a short phrase?

What do you notice if you speak it out loud or write it down? 'I intend to...' Does that make it stronger, or do you notice some kind of contraction coming up in response? Can you let that be as it is, and stay connected to the intention anyway?

Now set your timer, do your practice, and enjoy the clarity of purpose.

Each of the practices in this book gives you a clear intention to work with — for example the intention of the exercise above is to find your intention — but it's still worth listening for any additional personal element that you're bringing to the occasion.

When I dance, there's one underlying intention that is always there for me: to be filled with the Holy Spirit, Vast Mystery, God, Love, Consciousness, Presence, Divine Intelligence. To experience myself as moved by that. That's my longing and my prayer, and each breath is a communion. As I get older, I find myself cherishing this more and more. But there's often another layer of intention in addition to that, and it's helpful to know what that is.

It doesn't matter what your beliefs are for the purposes of using this book, but if you do have a sense of… whatever you want to call it… then you might want to get conscious about your own longing, intention and perceptions with regards to that.

Just as you might not always use a timer or might not always clear up last night's glasses, so you might not always want to name your intention. I dislike having an '*always!*' around anything — for me, that makes it routine and lifeless — but being clear about the intention for your practice is well worth including in your setup, forming good solid ground together with the sense of your timing and your space.

Music

> *I'm trying out a class with a teacher I have not worked with before. She has a small portable tape deck for a room full of thirty people so the sound quality is totally poxy, and her music choice is terrible. As an audiophile, I'm dying.*
>
> *I'm also determined though, so I take the experience I'm having and pour it through my movement. All the judgements ('This music is shit!' 'She's doing a terrible job!') and all the whining ('I can't dance to this!') becomes movement, and the feelings underneath it begin to intensify. The rage, the disappointment, the hopelessness. Soon I'm writhing around, almost foaming at the mouth. It's ridiculous, really. Except it's not.*
>
> *Next thing I know, I am sitting opposite someone looking at me with kindness in their eyes and my heart has broken open. Tears pouring down my face, I am beyond grateful to be alive, having one of the sweetest moments of my whole life.*

Like most people, I love music so much that it's hard to imagine life without it. It can be invaluable medicine, no question. However, you don't *need* music to practise! In fact, your relationship to movement will deepen and strengthen if you regularly do without it. Music is liquid inspiration, but if you depend on it, you'll be burdened with two consequences that are far from desirable.

Firstly, it'll be harder to find inspiration and motivation within yourself. Practising without music will challenge you in ways that create hotlines to internal sources of inspiration, and that's gold because they will always be there, no matter what your circumstance.

Thanks to countless hours practising in silence, in the scenario above I was able to be more interested in my inner experience than the crap music. And of course, it wasn't really about the music at all. Those thoughts and feelings took me right into primal trauma, where I simply did not want to be here, in this body, on this planet, having this life. It was absolutely profound, and it would not have happened if I had truly believed the music was important. I probably would have walked out, or waited for it to be over, vaguely faking presence. As it was, I healed something that day, and I'll always be ironically appreciative of that teacher's poor craftsmanship.

Practising without music at home created a solid foundation that gave me the self-belief and strength to do what I did that day. Make it part of your practice too. You'll acquire the ability to ruthlessly value your inner experience and follow it with curiosity, no matter what. Strong stuff.

The second undesirable consequence of always using music is that you'll reinforce the completely erroneous belief that you have to be inspired to move. Learn to practise with no dramas going on; not even inspiration. Move because you've chosen to. Find out what it's like to move when things are ordinary, dry, down to earth.

Learn to value movement for its own sake, not just for the altered state it can take you into. Get fascinated by your body's ways, without any deep and meaningful overlay.

Simple.

No big deal.

Moving without music will help you find it.

That way, when profound experience comes, you'll be much better equipped to handle it and stay with the grounded resource of your movement, no matter whether there's any music or not.

If you *do* choose to move with music, you'll find that many of your favourite teachers have playlists online, though many of them are rather long for regular home practice in my opinion. You'll find shorter mixes available from me online, with more to come especially created as a companion to this book.

I'm not advocating that you always practise in silence; just that you are *able* to. Music can be a great tool to get you out of your comfort zones, or to give you structure, or just for the delicious pleasure it brings.

Inspiration from outside is wonderful, as long as you're not dependent on it.

Once you've got space to move physically without hurting yourself, time to be there without interruption and a clear sense of your intention, then you're well prepared to take some inner journeys.

Ready?

Part II: Pathways in Practice

7. Ways to Practise

There are a thousand ways to kiss the ground!
A thousand ways to find your way home. — Rumi

If you've already fallen in love with a particular practice, for example ZeroOne, 5Rhythms, Open Floor or any of the other modalities out there (see Appendix I), you'll have learnt some specific structures to move through. If you're new to movement as a practice, then you'll get plenty of ideas from this book.

However, no matter what form or style you prefer, there are four main ways you can approach movement and dance, all of which are centred around a core practice of awareness.

The four practice modes are:

1. *Open*: Simply showing up, as you are. It doesn't matter what you do, it's just about being on the dance floor again today. Everything is valid and useful.
2. *Focus*: Choosing something specific to practise. It does matter what you do. Know what needs working on, create a structure for that purpose, then go for it.
3. *Surrender*: Let go, and let the dance take you. There are times when life just takes over. You're gone. In bliss, or in the abyss, it's total.
4. *Give*: Out there in the world, let yourself shine. The truth is, movement is powerful and it will allow you to grow. Share some of what you've found just by being yourself. Let that brilliance show.

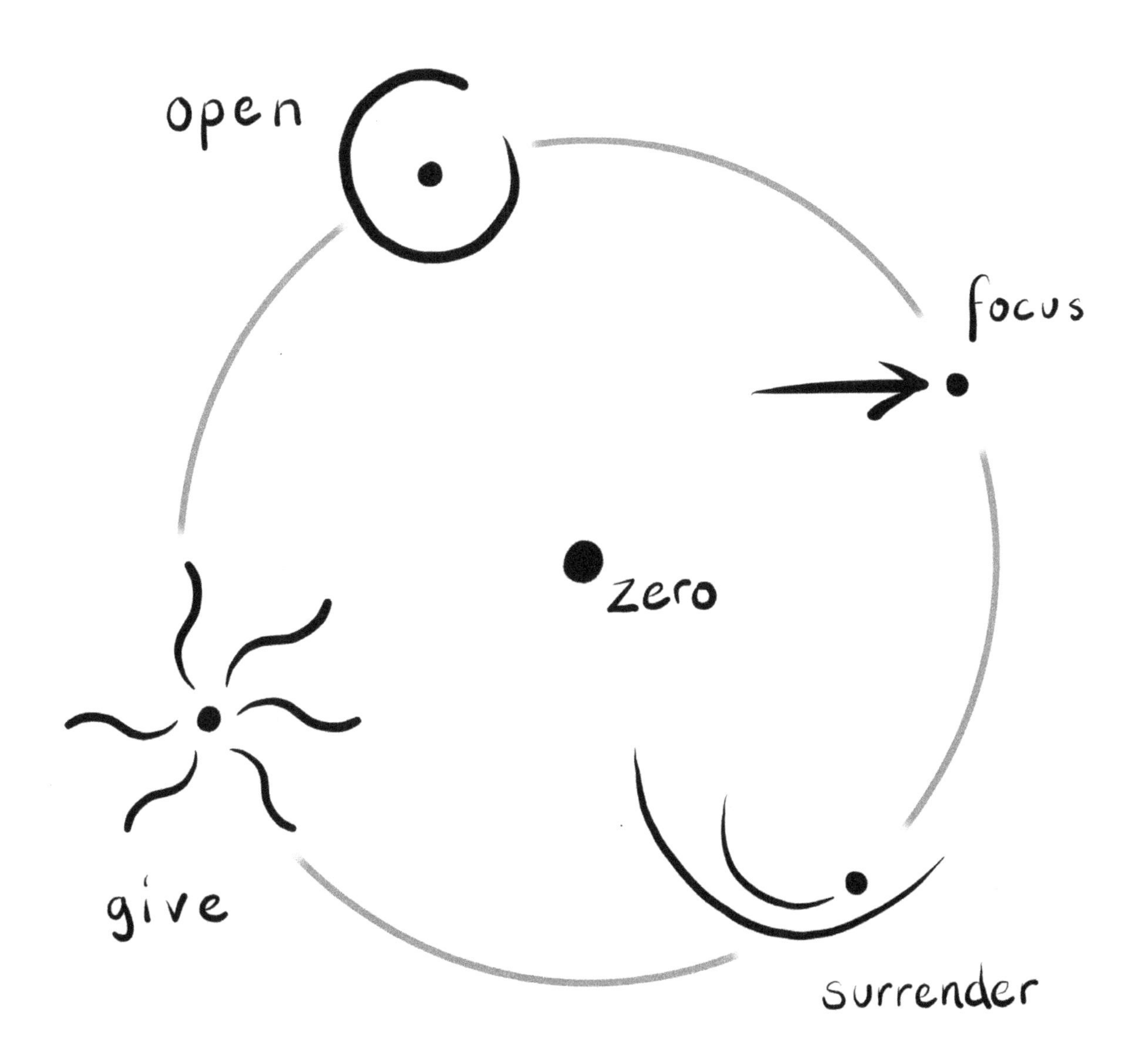
open
focus
zero
give
surrender

To be healthy, and to flourish in the long term, your practice will need to include all four of these modes. The first three — *Open, Focus and Surrender* — all happen on the dance floor during your dedicated practice time, and will keep your experience in movement growing and deepening.

The fourth — *Give* — happens out there in the rest of your life, forming a bridge from your dance floor across to everything else. It plays an essential role, integrating your movement work into the fabric of your day-to-day existence and allowing the benefits you find in your practice to be simply and naturally shared with the world, turning your personal steps into something that's meaningful for everyone.

These four modes of practice form a kind of cycle, each one tending to emerge from the other. To Give out there in the world is an effortless overflowing of your cup once you've Surrendered on the dance floor. Surrender will inevitably come to you if you Focus on your stuff, turning your personal issues into movement enquiry. Focused practice will become a natural next step if you keep showing up, Open to whatever arises.

You will also notice the central element to this cycle, that I've called *Zero*. By this I mean the presence practice that is the essence of all meditation; the simple attention to the present moment which is the core of all four practice modes. Zero is central to your practice, but you may not notice that for a long, long time. I didn't. I was so entranced by the power of movement that I didn't notice the still, silent presence that was within everything I did. That came to me gradually over the course of many years. Zero is the beginning, the end, and the fulcrum of your practice, but it's far more subtle than the four practice modes, so we'll start with the movement and come back to Zero later.

You'll find notes on each of these practice modes in the following pages with a mix of encouragement, inspiration and practical tools. No doubt you will be able to add to what I've written once you delve into the experience for yourself, taking the journey through your unique inner wilderness, unmapped by anyone else, where your practice will be wholly yours.

Over time, you become what you do. You are your practices, whether that's moving your body, speaking the truth, or scrolling a phone. But movement as meditation is powerful, so in the ratio of time in to results out, the minutes you spend on it will have a far bigger impact that almost anything else you do.

8. Open

Let go of how you thought your life should be, and embrace the life that is trying to work its way into your consciousness. — Caroline Myss

an ordinary day
this movement now
totally unique

breathing body turned
a thousand times like this
but never here before

I am my body, my heart, my mind
I am this move, this feeling, this knowing
one seamless creative flow, no goal in sight
other than this longing for the honesty of my body's ways
beyond my small tangle of concerns
to show me once more that I am alive and free

this dance
this breath
this glance

there is no 'me'
only this
now

open

. . . in which you simply show up to be with your body, your breath and your experience, Open to whatever comes.

In this stage of practice, it's all good. Showing up is the thing. It doesn't matter what you 'do' – just get yourself onto the dance floor and spend some time there, discovering what comes naturally to you today. Move with or without music, with or without structure, with no goal other than to be present with yourself as an embodied experience, willing to move beyond 'normal' or stay totally ordinary, breathing deeper than usual and welcoming whatever comes up as a guest, whatever comes from life itself.

Your dance is your life force, expressed through your moving body. Breath made visible. Welcome it, however it appears. Get to know it, one day at a time.

There are times when my 'movement' practice has essentially involved lying almost entirely still on the floor, and I've come to see that those sessions are every bit as valuable as the times when I've been uber-dynamic and inspired. Get on the floor, with your feet or your whole body, and devote some time to being physical.

If you have a favourite modality (see Appendix I) you can use that, but it's not necessary to use any structure at all. In Open practice, the thing is to simply be there, willing.

Some days you'll be tired, others full of life. Sometimes you'll feel creative and inspired, others you'll wonder what the point is and seriously consider scrolling your phone instead. Some days you won't merely consider bailing out like that; you will. (When that happens, it's important that you don't bash yourself into the ground with recriminations. Just show up again the next day, ready to Open once more.)

In essence: Take a step; be present with whatever's going on; repeat.

That sounds simple, but it actually takes a lot of practice and a lot of working through stuff to be able to do that consistently for more than a few seconds, because we have so many internal restrictions impeding our natural birthright to be totally alive, loving and free.

That's where cycling through all four stages of movement practice comes in. But let's not get ahead of ourselves — let's look at what Open practice could be in more detail.

Practise: When you feel good, Open (≥3m)

You've slept well and have no aches and pains, there are no big dramas going on emotionally, and your mind is clear to concentrate on the moment:

Decide how long to devote to your practice, either preparing some music or setting your timer if you're working in silence, and off you go. Let the movements of your body draw you in, making you aware of physical sensations and allowing any emotions that arise to be expressed through the movement. It's like following a path in the wilderness — a path where you cannot see the way ahead but which magically appears each time you put your foot down. Simply stay present with your experience as best you can, no matter where it takes you, Guided by the natural, spontaneous movements of your body, Open to yourself again and again.

Practice: When you feel lousy, Open (≥3m)

Your knee hurts, the neighbours kept you awake half the night and you want to hit someone. Your mind is haranguing you with a bulging to-do list and you'd rather drink coffee and drown in the news headlines... yes... exactly the same practice as if you were feeling good:

Decide how long to devote to your practice, either preparing some music or setting your timer if you're working in silence, and off you go. Let the movements of your body draw you in, making you aware of physical sensations and allowing any emotions that arise to be expressed through the movement. It's like following a path in the wilderness — a path where you cannot see the way ahead but which magically appears each time you put your foot down. Simply stay present with your experience as best you can, no matter where it takes you, Guided by the natural, spontaneous movements of your body, Open to yourself again and again.

It doesn't matter how you feel: just show up and drop into your practice. Good days, bad days, numb days, electric days, ordinary days. Set aside a little time and devote yourself to being physical.

There are three things that happen when you move like this, any of which can be radical and life-changing or down-to-earth and no big deal.

- *Getting out of your head.* Yes, that incessant nagging of your thinking mind is a thing. Much of the time it's a drag, but you can get more practised at turning your attention elsewhere, noticing what's going on in your body, feeling what's going on emotionally, sensing what you know in your depths, in the aspects of your mind that are rooted in your body, not just in your head.
- *Experience your true nature directly.* It's all too easy to spend time cut off from what's going on deep inside, driven by deadlines or expectations of what's socially acceptable. But once you start to move, things get real, fast. As the renowned dancer Martha Graham said, 'The body cannot lie.' Movement will reveal the state you're in, if you pay attention.
- *Things will change.* Movement will show you where you're at, but it will also tend to stir up that state of being and catalyse change. As a human being, you are an organic life-form that is designed to grow and evolve throughout your lifetime, like an endlessly unfolding flower with more petals, shapes and colours always waiting to come forth. The combination of moving your body, breathing deeply and paying attention, with a willingness to Open as you go, will accelerate the process. You'll become more alive, and life is change.

Dropping into Open practice is a highly effective way to get out of your head, get to know yourself, and grow up a little more. Make sure you are aware of your whole body, and your breath, then pay attention to what comes up for you, making space for everything to be as it is, even if it is uncomfortable.

In this way, you're practising being yourself. 'Be yourself' is easy to say, but the reality is that at any given moment we mostly have almost no idea who we are. We're conscious of a little bit, but vast unexplored areas exist beyond that, full of dark shadows, superpowers, lost children and indescribable mysteries.

Who you *truly* are is a work-in-progress of infinite potential, a miracle of creation, a Buddha in the making. But who you experience yourself to be in the moment is... well, what would you say? For the most part, not exactly infinite or miraculous, if you're anything like me.

I've been dogged by deeply ingrained perceptions of limitation and failure all my life, and as often as not, I still am. However, I have learnt not to automatically believe what I think. Countless times I've shown up on the dance floor feeling for all the world like I'm trussed up in thick ropes, but by the end of the session I'm full of a fiery sense of freedom and zest for life. Or I've begun feeling strong and purposeful only to find myself falling into a deeply vulnerable state which, while a nuisance if I want to achieve a lot that day, has an almost unbearable lightness and sweetness, like coming home.

Once I'm moving, who I am experiencing myself to be often doesn't last long. I practise being myself whilst staying open to changing, and I'm suggesting you do the same.

Micro-Practices

> *One day I show up for my practice and have a brief check-in with myself about what to work with today. Immediately I have a strong sense, almost a voice telling me, 'Don't dance today!'.*
>
> *I'm rather taken aback, because I so firmly believe that everyday practice is 'good' and skipping it is 'bad'. But the instruction is so clear I decide to try it out.*
>
> *The next day, the same thing happens. And the next. On the third day, I blow a fuse. There's so much energy coursing through me that I have to let it out, there and then in the kitchen whilst making lunch. I jump around and shout out loud, doing a little dance whilst washing lettuce.*

As I said earlier, for many years, I danced every day for an hour. I learnt a great deal, grew stronger and more supple psychologically as well as physically, and became skilled in some ways. That approach had a drawback though, which I had no inkling of until I let it go.

I'd been using my practice as a safety valve, blowing off steam so that I could stay 'normal' the rest of the time. Once I took that away my vitality, passion and energy had to find expression in other ways, encouraging me to open the box and effectively be 'in practice' 24/7. But it also got me started with the kind of 'micro-practice' I had with the lettuce – entering into movement or meditation whilst in the middle of everyday moments.

I'm a great fan of these micro-practices, peppering the day with tuning into my body, breath and feelings, noticing what wants to happen and allowing it. Maybe you do this already, but if not, I'd strongly suggest you add them to the mix: simple Open practice moments where you drop into a dance for a few seconds, take one extra deep breath with total attention, or pause what you're doing and sense into your body.

Micro-practices are great to break up a workday or a long drive. They're also great for cooking, when you can put on some tunes to spice yourself up along with the food. They're great for passionate moments (heavenly or hellish) with your loved ones, to break out of normal for a moment and get physical with someone, in touch or not. Kids love them, as long as you play it at their level and don't freak them out.

Practise: Microdance (20s max!)

i) You've been busy with tasks for a while, and have a moment spare. You're in a queue at the market. You've been rushing for a train, plane, appointment, and once you arrive, there's some time to wait. Instead of immediately getting out your phone; pause. Relax your muscles, drop your shoulders, settle into stillness. Breathe. Notice what's going on inside.

ii) You're feeling emotional in some way, and in private. Take 20 seconds to find the shapes it wants to make, breathing deep and allowing some of that energy to release through movement.

iii) You're feeling emotional in some way, in a place where it would not be appropriate to express it. Feel your feet on the floor or bum on seat, the sense of gravity holding you. Notice how the feelings are manifesting in your body and breathe into those sensations, allowing the feelings to circulate a little more freely through you. Listen for any action that the feelings are wanting — how could you creatively and appropriately allow that to happen?

iv) You're shopping for new clothes, and a great track comes on. Imperceptibly, you shift your weight back and forth in time with the beat and let a smile break out on your face.

v) You're shopping for new clothes, and a great track comes on. For a few seconds you break right out in some wild and fine moves, to the surprise and delight of everyone around you.

The other day I had a rush of delight in the kitchen with a friend, when we literally jumped for joy, bouncing around while we both giggled at how silly it is sometimes, being human. It was all over in thirty seconds, but it was incredibly refreshing and changed my whole day.

This is where the word 'practice' becomes daft, ostentatious for a simple lovely moment, but the truth is, if I didn't have the ease of expressing my feelings physically which comes from dedicated 'practice', I probably would not have bounced. And bouncing is fun.

Opening Endnotes

> *I'm in practice, Open mode. Nothing particular going on. Abruptly, I sense my body wanting to move close to the ground. I go down on all fours with no idea of what's coming, but quickly find myself writhing around in bizarre tortuous movements. I drop into the feeling-quality that's emerging through the movement, and am immediately sucked down into the underworld, Persephone with limbs akimbo.*
>
> *The experience happening in my body is one of being tortured. There is vivid imagery coming up, so gross that I will not describe it here, along with a full-body need to scream out and thrash around on the floorboards. The strange thing is, it feels in some way satisfying, like when you have a massage and the therapist goes deep into a sore muscle in just the right way: it's painful, but it's a relief.*
>
> *Right there on the floor, I know in my bones that I've been living with this pain and terror all my life, and that now I'm finally getting to feel it, allowing it to release through my movements. It feels incredibly 'right'.*
>
> *Also, I know I can snap out of it any time I wish to. I do so, just to check, because the thought of being stuck there is scary. I snap back into 'normal' but can feel the darkness rumbling around inside me still, so I drop back in again, curious to go further. Immediately the whole thing is right there again, like going back into a dream. I stay with it until it seems to fade and come to a natural ending, where I just know that I'm done.*

In the course of our daily ordinariness, life has a way of bowling curve balls to us at precisely the right time to bump us awake, often in rather uncomfortable ways.

Open practice is just the same. It won't always be enjoyable. You'll come up against states of being that are difficult, sometimes in precisely the ways you don't want to deal with. That doesn't mean there's anything 'wrong', despite it feeling that way. On the contrary, you could get fascinated with the sense of wrongness and dive into it, approaching the moment as an opportunity to open another door within you, and get to know yourself better.

The dance described above was many years ago now. I shall never forget the strange paradox of finding such a tortured quality satisfying because of allowing myself to inhabit it, fully embodied. I have no idea whether it was a snapshot of my pre-verbal experience, some kind of past life flashback, or an epigenetic ancestral memory. It can stay as a mystery, but I know that the feelings in my body were real, and I know

I released something traumatic from my system that day.

The fact that I could go through something like that alone, in my little dance space between the living room and the kitchen, with no music and no therapist, is marvellous to me. I'm sure you could too. It just takes a little faith in your true nature, some courage and curiosity, and a willingness to be taken beyond what you know.

I tell this story to illustrate how far we can go if we simply Open to the moment. We are all born with the capacity to feel deeply, and to heal naturally. It's more a case of learning how to get out of your own way than learning any fancy techniques. Your body knows.

If we took Open practice all the way, consistently, it would open every door we have.

However, in case you're now feeling anxious about what you might be letting yourself in for, let me reassure you: if you stay with what feels OK for you in your body, and go with that rather than following an idea of what you think you *should* be doing, you are unlikely to get out of your depth before you're ready to swim, or learnt to breathe underwater. I'd been a dedicated dancer for a few years by the time I had that tortuous experience. I was ready for it. (If you're concerned about this, do have a read of Appendix II on trauma.)

If anything, the problem tends to be the other way around – it can be hard to find the doorway that takes us beyond what we're used to and comfortable with. We develop highly effective defence mechanisms around our blindspots and vulnerabilities. Most of the time, if we're heading towards those danger zones, long before we're aware of anything, the psyche will throw up a smokescreen so fast and subtle we don't even notice it.

Instead, what we notice *is* that we're tired, or bored, or the music's not right, or there are too many other things to do, or it's too cold or too hot, or we suddenly think we'd be better off doing a different practice today. It seems like something's wrong.

The truth is, there *is* something 'wrong', or at least misaligned, but the problem is not what your thoughts are telling you. The problem is that you're far more magnificent and miraculous than you think, and you're scared of going through the gateway that lies between where you are right now and where you could be if you dared. That fear moves incredibly fast, and it's mostly invisible to you because you've lived with it all your life. You've got so used to its presence that you don't notice it. It seems like 'the way things are'.

Open practice is the discipline of continuing to follow, learn, be a disciple of whatever comes up, including any sense of discomfort. Get curious about it, lean into it, get to know yourself through it.

And, when you find a blockage, a serious difficulty or something you'd like to change, maybe you're ready to give it some *Focus*.

9. Focus

What you want most will be found where you least want to look.
— Carl Jung

Today, something has to change

I am willing

Not just allowing, but adding the force of my will

Like you might add chilli sauce to a good meal:

A determined melding of discontent and desire

I will feel this fear

expand this joy

aim for this vision

open this box

dive through this darkness

emerge into this light

understand my father

let go of my mother

respect my sister

forgive my brother

I hold the intent of my Focus

Not tense, but clear and true

Aiming right at it

Along the path that takes me through

Ohhhh!!!.... the struggle!....

The fears, the resistance, the doubts

Tugging at my commitment

I add them to the dance

So the fire gets fuelled still hotter, and

The mix gets mashed still further

Through each thrashing move and panting breath

And before I know it,

I'm through to the other side

Astonished at the clear view

And en-lightened heart

So glad to be here

Again

. . . in which you take your life issues and give them attention.

Focus your practice on them.

One at a time.

While Open practice is vital, continuing with only this mode you're likely to eventually be lost within a comfort zone, going around in small circles. It's time to call yourself on some blind spots, ask some uncomfortable questions, get real about what you avoid and look for ways to make some changes.

It's time to Focus.

Yes, Open practice is a profound resource. Naturally, your movement will be that way sometimes, just going with the flow. But you'll learn faster and deeper if you also Focus your attention on specific blockages, patterns and desires for growth, finding creative ways to work with them.

In approaching a time of Focus, questions work well. Here are a few of my favourites:

- Are there areas of your body where you tend to lose consciousness? Or that don't move much?
- Do you tend to lead with the same parts of your body all the time?
- Do you always begin a movement session in the same way?
- Are you free to move on all levels or do you tend to always stay on your feet?
- Do you breathe consciously?
  Through your mouth as well as your nose, or does your mouth shut by default?
- Can you embody your sexual energy?
- Do you tend to be repressed emotionally, or are you addicted to dramas, becoming uneasy if things get too peaceful?
- Which emotions are particularly taboo for you to express, or even allow yourself to feel?

- Do you notice when your voice needs to come out with sounds, shouts, cries, moans, whoops? Do you allow that? If not, why not? What would it take?
- What moves you?
- What do you fear?
- What pisses you off?
- What are you grieving for?
- What delights you?
- What do you care deeply about?
- What aspect of intimacy do you most avoid?
- Who do you most fear being judged or criticised by? For doing what, exactly?
- How are things with your parents? Your siblings? Your partner? Your ex-partners?
- What conflicts are you embroiled in?
- Who do you most vehemently write off as 'bad', or 'other'?
- What do you worry about in the middle of the night?
- Do you dare to look soberly at what's happening for us humans right now, in the context of what you can see happening to the earth?
- What do you long for?
- Are you doing paid work that is meaningful to you?
  How do you shine, or what do you give, in other ways?
- What do you live for?

What are you waiting for?

Practise: See yourself (≥20m)

It can be incredibly informative to record yourself moving. Ask your inner critic to take a break: tune into that critical part of you, and gently tell them that you're about to do something that will work better if they are not directing. Tell them that you know they see a lot, and are very intelligent, but you need them to sit out this time. They can come back later.

Set up a camera so that you can see your whole body in the video. Warm up so you're engaged and alive all over, then set the video recording and move freestyle for three minutes.

Now watch the recording, looking for patterns as though you're a brilliant movement coach who has your best interests at heart, wanting to help yourself find some practical next steps to work with.

Give these questions to your compassionate intelligence, using pen and paper:

i) How do you feel in your body as you watch yourself move? What comes up for you? Can you be kind with yourself around that, especially if it's painful?

ii) What can you see that you're doing well, that you appreciate? Write it this way: 'I appreciate myself for...'

iii) What would be a good next step for you to Focus on as a movement practitioner?

Whether you film yourself or not, when you are dancing, what do you notice about yourself? When you are living your daily life, what do you notice about yourself? What are your patterns? Your Focus doesn't have to be something you dislike and want to move on from – it could be something that you believe you have the potential for, and desire to grow into.

Take one thing, and work with it. The more specific, detailed and personal, the better.

For example, if you tend to always begin a movement session the same way, experiment with trying something different and notice what comes up for you as you do so. Be curious about any resistance –

really curious — enough to get to know the feelings and beliefs hidden in the 'I don't like this.'

Or if you tend to live fearfully, playing it safe and staying within what you know, then spend some time Focusing on your fears. Don't do this vaguely. Get specific: write down all the things that scare you, then pick one of them and make it as detailed as possible.

I first did that in my early thirties, in mentorship with Gabrielle. My top pick was 'Being judged', but she wouldn't let me stop there. She asked me to name the person or kind of person I was most afraid of being judged by (father figures I had respect for) and for what (being in my sexual energy) and then to dance through *that specific fear*. It was electric.

When you develop your ability to Focus your practice like this, you'll go deeper within yourself, wrestling with your psyche in profound ways that have the potential to change your life. You'll encounter places within you that are like hidden children, parts of you that got lost along the way at times when you either got too little of what you needed, or too much of what you didn't need. You will probably unearth strong feelings, discover your strengths and weaknesses, and develop abilities you didn't know you had.

In this way, your practice can be highly therapeutic. However, that does not mean you are engaging in therapy per se. I would describe the kinds of practice in this book as blend of healing, meditation and — crucially — art.

Movement as Art, Healing, and Meditation

> *I'm not getting what I think I want with Maria-Carin. A young part of me is not getting what he needs. I'm feeling resentful, and being quietly destructive.*
>
> *In a moment of grace, I see what's happening and manage to make it physical. Shoulders hunching forward, lips pouting, fists clenched, I growl at her and we both burst out laughing. We're laughing because it's so true, and so tragic.*
>
> *A few days later I'll be doing the same thing all over again, but it doesn't have quite the same weight. Neither of us can buy into it so thoroughly because we've both seen it clearly. The patterns don't go away, but we can bring more consciousness to them, which loosens their grip.*

You are engaged in healing, in the sense that it will make you more whole, reintegrating lost parts of yourself. You are engaged in meditation, in the sense that you're practising being present in this moment. But vitally, there is a third foundational ingredient that will give your work stability: the *art* of movement and dance. And I do mean art. This is what saves your practice from getting lost in the vortex of your wounded inner child. Any time you find that you're taking yourself too seriously, or believe yourself to be either worse or better than everyone else, you know you're in that vortex, caught in a mélange of self-pity and self-importance. In the healing process, there's a place for allowing that to be as it is. But learning to pour whatever you feel into dance is so liberating partly because an element of what you're doing is creating art. You are taking the raw material of your human experience and getting creative with it. It's a seismic change of attitude.

If you're feeling deeply troubled, could you be troubled brilliantly? Could you become a moving, breathing, crying-out-loud work of art that communicates those troubles to the very earth you are dancing on?

This takes practice. You can get better at it over time, just as if you were learning to play a musical instrument. The payoff is that this creative approach to your inner state can work its way into your daily life, for example making the business of relating a far more interesting challenge than all that endless talking we can get into.

I can gain consciousness of my unmet needs, such as in the example above, because of the ten thousand times I've turned my personal tragedies into art. It can be quite a wrench when I'm in the depths, but with practice, it does come easier.

A word of caution though: are you impatient with your fear and pain, wishing it would all go away? As I said, these places can be hidden children within us, and it can be all too easy to treat them cruelly. Longing for the pain to go away, we can use the zeal of the artist to subtly banish the wounded child still further, which will only add more loops to your journey.

To make art requires daring and risk, whilst to heal we need safety and gentleness. We have to learn to feel how vulnerable we truly are. It's a delicate balance, walking back home to yourself with integrity. Value all three foundational ingredients: the simple presence of meditation, tenderness of healing, and the bold strokes of art. Often one will be more prevalent than another, but if you keep them reasonably balanced over time, you'll be giving your practice a good chance of staying healthy.

In this way, you can use movement to grow and learn through any state of being, no matter what it is. Everything you can experience has a dance. No exceptions. As someone in a workshop with me said recently, 'How can I dance shame? When I think of shame, I'm just collapsed, not moving.' My response was to say, 'If you stay with the sensations going on in your body whilst you're collapsed, that's a dance in itself, even if you're apparently motionless. Yet although you think it will be that way, the reality may be different. Approach it with the tenderness and compassion of a healer, the curiosity and ardour of an artist, the stillness and silence of a monk in meditation. What comes if you stay with it, keep going through, listening to your breath, allowing your body to shape itself beyond anything that's normal for you?'

Focused practice can take you deep into emotional and psychological shadowlands. Make sure to have some grounding in movement, such as in *Basics* (Chapter 6) if you want to proceed in a balanced and effective way. One step at a time.

Then, begin your exploration of Focus with the physical.

Focusing on Physical

> *I am working with a group after lunch and everyone is spaced out, tired and floppy. Their movement is uninspired, vague, listless. I turn the music off, and we move with our Focus on one part of the body at a time. Elbows, knees, hands, hips. Within minutes, the room has transformed. Everyone is awake, paying attention to the moment, engaged with their movement. The atmosphere is electric with creativity and presence.*

Focused practice changes things; it makes stuff happen. The body is an endless resource, and working with your physical patterns is both catalytic and grounding at the same time.

Practise: body tune-in (≥10m)

Focus on one part of your body at a time. Experiment with how it can move, or how it wants to move. Breathe with it. Then let the rest of your body follow its lead, learning new ways to dance from its example.

Shift your Focus to a different part and repeat the process, going through your whole body as a sequence, for example feet, legs, hips, torso, head, shoulders, arms, hands. You could choose larger areas such as front to back, left side to right side, or you could work in great detail, including your internal organs.

This Focus will help you to:

- Become more intimately acquainted with your whole body.
- Strengthen your ability to pay attention steadily on one thing.
- Practise the arts of being a leader and a team player — one part leads, the rest of your body is the team.

Is there an area of your body that's troubling you? How about giving that the Focus one day and letting it speak through movement, breath, sounds, and shapes? Then get pen and paper and let that part of you speak in words.

Is there a part of your body that you identify with strongly, that you like, and another part that you feel estranged from? How about Focusing on each in turn, and then getting them to dance with each other like partners, feeling the connection between them? Have them write to each other after moving for a while?

The exciting thing about working with a physical Focus is its capacity to take you into movement states and shapes that are unusual for you. Go for it! Let the Focus take you down on the floor, under the table, or brandishing an umbrella. Let it bring weird sounds out from you or distort your face. Let it generate strange shakes, percussive bursts, unseemly droops or jumps, mysterious pauses where you don't know what's happening. Be willing to be surprised.

Let the Focus teach you new ways of being with and within your body.

Focusing on Feelings

> *I am preparing lunch, chopping vegetables for a soup. I can sense that I've got something going on emotionally, deep down, and I'm not sure what it is. A professional shadow-sleuth, I breathe into the hiddenness while I dice a carrot, loosening my spine a little, enlivening my whole body in order to allow it to surface.*
>
> *Then it hits me: I'm happy. Wow, that surprised me. My face cracks like an old mask as I let a smile break through. I had been suppressing a smile. So unused to that feeling, it just didn't occur to me.*

We're born with the instinctive ability to express our feelings physically. Babies don't have a problem embodying their emotional experience — it's natural. We just got trained out of it.

Often we use the phrase 'expressing feelings' to mean 'describing in words what I feel whilst remaining impassive'. Talking *about* your feelings is not expression, it's a report. Emotional expression involves allowing your feelings to show in your face, move through your body and be heard in the tone of your voice.

Emotional energy is often uncomfortable, and most of us have picked up all kinds of techniques for handling our feelings that involve a lot of thinking, mostly designed to distance us from the discomfort. However, we can re-learn and remember how to allow our bodies to handle all that energy. Instead of civilising our wild-at-heart nature, we can use our practice to develop the instincts we're born with, bringing them to maturity.

Kids naturally jump for joy, and most of us find that kind of pleasurable feeling-state relatively easy to be with. The 'negative' emotions of fear, anger and sadness (including all their variations such as anxiety and panic, rage and resentment, melancholy and despair) are more painful to experience, and we tend to want to get away from them or get them out of our system. Their fundamental nature is not negative at all though, but rather life-preserving and essential. These painful feelings are emotional energies that we naturally have available to us throughout our lives, just like every other mammal, and are designed to keep us alive and well.

Fear gives us the impetus and propulsion needed to change or get out of the way of danger, fast. Anger deals with threats that we cannot escape and empowers our ability to change things outside of ourselves. Sadness allows us to let go of what we have been attached to, and when experienced open-heartedly, leaves us cleansed and ready for new joys and loves.

Feelings are energy, and can be used in destructive or creative ways. It's the stories we have woven into them that determine our experience of them, and those stories are not the feelings themselves.

Using movement to explore, express and release emotions is a radical, life-affirming pathway that has the potential to connect you with the raw energy of your heart. It can awaken your whole being as more alive and open-hearted, clearer in your choices and your relations with others. To dance your fears is to become empowered through them, to grow up. To dance your anger is to take full responsibility for it, able to use it in a healthy way that benefits everyone. To dance your sorrows is to go beyond self-pity, leaving you broken open and wise to the depth of your humanity. To dance your joy is to become generous with it and find your way in the world. To embrace all of these together is to love. To love fully.

These fundamentals are there for all of us, but the precise way they map out for you is unique. You have to get to know your own heart — lights, shadows, strengths and wounded places.

When exploring your emotions, you might choose to Focus on a feeling that you're overly full of, releasing old stuck packets of it from your body and creating more consciousness, space and freedom around it. For example, you can't get rid of the pure spirit of fear given to us all for survival, but you can loosen, express and release childhood knots of fear-with-story woven into your body long ago.

Alternatively, you may choose to Focus on an emotion that you rarely experience in daily life in order to fully access its gifts and power. In this case, it may be hard for you to feel it at first. If you've spent a lifetime in denial of your anger, for example, you may have to conduct an ongoing research project for some time before you connect with it easily. Be curious, patient and creatively intelligent – *why* have you grown up denying your anger? Find out. Dance your denial. What are your beliefs about anger? Are you certain that those beliefs are true, or could there be different ways of seeing? Write about it. Draw an image of the blockage in relation to the anger. Search through your body for the fear of the anger, and breathe into *that*, move with *that*. Desire to find it and have faith that it's there (it is).

Growing up as I did, with a vast underworld of suppressed pain and fear inside me, it was a tremendous liberation to begin to get conscious of it and to express it through dance. I would eagerly go into the shadow realms and wade through deep existential terrors, volcanic furies, oceans of grief. It was such a relief to *feel* that stuff. I got used to tracking the scent of some buried emotional hell-realm surfacing, giving it space and finding its expression physically. Little did I suspect that even more buried than those painful feelings was my joy.

After that experience I had chopping vegetables, I gave myself the homework of Focusing on joy and lightness. It is still work in progress, but I do it fairly regularly and it's helpful in opening up that pathway.

If you're rather numb emotionally, I would not recommend using your mind to make yourself feel something, for instance conjuring up the memory of the last time someone pissed you off. Instead, trust that your anger is there within you, have the desire to feel it, then open yourself physically to its energy by moving your whole body whilst breathing through your mouth. Particularly *exhaling* through your mouth will allow your feelings to arise much more easily – catalysing your feelings whilst having your mouth shut is like driving with one foot on the accelerator and the other on the brake. Make yourself available in these ways and then trust the process. If you've sat on your anger for decades, it may take a lot of practice to release it, but better you experience it genuinely and naturally than manipulate yourself into feeling using your mind.

Or maybe rather than being numb you get flooded easily. If you become overwhelmed, you could take the artist's path and dance the state of 'overwhelmed'. That's a wild one that I personally love, but it's not everyone's cup of tea. Alternatively, you could take the more gentle approach, safer for the little ones inside you, and slow down using any of the methods described in *Foundations* (Chapter 6) to settle your nervous system. Which of those choices works for you is for you to find out. Get to know your own inner landscape, and how best to navigate it, by trying things out.

You may start off Focusing on one particular emotion and then find that it changes during your practice time. Following the flow of your own heart as it morphs and shape-shifts will teach you a lot about yourself and is a totally valid way to go. On the other hand, maybe that's something you always do as a kind of escape. For example, many people will toughen up into anger rather than stay with the vulnerability of fear, and others will collapse into sadness rather than stay with the fierce edge of anger. If you tend towards ways of avoiding your feelings in ways like that, you could learn a lot and create some new pathways by staying with your chosen Focus. Even as the old familiar escape route opens up, tugging you sideways with the gravitational pull of a habit that feels natural, you could practise staying with the more challenging and less known path straight ahead.

Another foundation stone of working with emotional energy is your voice. Feelings need to come out, and a strongly emotional body will often need to make sounds. Whimpering, moaning, shouting 'Yes!' or 'Fuck!' or 'Argh!', crying out loud, singing like a crazy person, or even whispering a secret can all be incredibly empowering and a huge relief. We're meant to make noises! It's hard on your body to hold that stuff in.

At our house we have shared walls with neighbours, and we've told them that we have a practice that sometimes involves using our voices, so they're not completely freaked out by it. Many people have great heavy cloaks of shame around being heard though, and fears of judgement. That's certainly been true for me, and I still have to get over a bit of a shyness-hump to use my voice in any way other than 'Nice Polite Englishman' style. It's so worth it though, and for me, there are times when letting my voice out is crucial, even more catalytic and freeing than moving.

Ready? Remember: practise when you don't need it so you have the skills when you're up shit creek. Having an emotional Focus is usually fascinating, often fun, and can be challenging enough to earn you a medal.

Practice: Focus on feelings (≥15m)  

Before you begin, let go of your expectations, willing to see what comes and be moved in unfamiliar ways. Tiny movements can be just the ticket. You might move like a crazed genius or deformed monster, a small child or an animal. Long periods of no movement at all can be a vital part of an exploration, especially when you stay present with what's happening in your body.

i) Decide which emotion to Focus on — for example, anxiety, resentment, joy. Whisper it to yourself, or shout it out loud to the world, or write it down: 'I choose to focus on .... [fill in the blank] for this session.'

ii) Before doing anything, take some time to feel: become still and listen inside yourself. Notice your body sensations. Scan for any sense of the feeling you're choosing to work with. Be with it. Make space for it. Notice any judgements that come up, thank them for their input and ask them to please stand aside for now so that you can be with the Focus of your choice. Be curious about how it feels to feel.

iii) When you're ready, enter into movement, either freestyle or using a structure from a modality you love. Invite your emotional energy to be felt, to be expressed, to find release and creative freedom.

You may find that when your feelings are running strongly, your arms, hands and shoulders steal the show, leaving the rest of you stuck. How could you include your whole body, valuing the movement of your feet, legs, hips and torso too?

Can you stay aware of your breath? Let the exhale come out of your mouth. This is incredibly effective in connecting your consciousness with your feelings and allowing your body to express and release your emotional energy. Let it OUT! Does your voice need to come too?

Don't rush to finish. Stay with the last traces of motion, and even then, wait a while. The time when the movement stops is valuable. Stay aware of your body, your breath, your feelings. Maybe take some time to write about your experience, either as a kind of travel journal or allowing the feeling itself to speak through your pen.

When you begin to go about the rest of your day, be aware that there's a subtle aftermath going on. Notice if you feel the need to talk to someone about it; that may be worth doing. Allow the experience to inform you, to influence you, integrating it into more 'normal' daily life moments. Let yourself be changed by the process.

Learning to move with an emotional Focus is a life-long path with the potential for enormous benefits, especially if you grew up repressed, suppressed and depressed, as I did. Slow and steady does it. Get some support from a skillful professional if you're consistently out of your depth. Consider telling someone you trust about your experience, so you're not on your own with it.

Focusing on Someone

My daughter, my mother, my wife and my sister are each struggling in their lives — all of them at the same time — and I'm really struggling with their pain. I am mired in an uncomfortable mix of mis-placed responsibility and resentment with each of them in different ways.

I choose an object to represent each of them, place one in each corner of the room, step into the middle and begin to dance. I dance with each one individually at first, then letting them engulf me, I go under. It's like drowning. Using movement, breath, sound and speech, I surrender to the overwhelm, letting the energy of all that emotion become fuel for movement rather than head-trips. Step by step, I find a sense of empowered centre within myself, a masculine match for the ocean of femininity surrounding me.

I came out of that session altered in relation to each of them, and at that time in my life something pivotal began to change generally for me around women. I slowly turned towards becoming more deep-down-honest, not haplessly saying 'yes' when the truth was 'no'. The marriage didn't last, and who knows, maybe that dance was partly a catalyst for its breakdown. It may have been. Getting more real does not guarantee an outcome that you might consciously believe is a good one.

How about you?

Who's troubling you? Who are you grateful for? Who do you want more depth with?

Focusing on 'someone' is a powerful tool. Use it boldly, with care. Be willing to feel a lot and to witness your mind changing.

Practise: Focusing on someone you know (≥15m)  

i) Decide who you are going to Focus on, then either use an object to represent them as I did, or write their name on a piece of paper. You could even just imagine them there. Place them somewhere in the room.

ii) Warm up for a few minutes until you feel rooted in your body.

iii) Begin to move in relation to them. Keep it simple at first, stepping or turning towards and away, noticing what sensations are coming up in your body. Notice your breath. Gradually go deeper, allowing your movement to get more experimental and expressive. Let your body make sounds if it wants to, especially if you're feeling emotional.

iv) What do you feel? How does your body communicate that to them? What do you understand? What do you see? What do you want? You could experiment with words, speaking out loud whatever you would actually like to say to them. (If you do use words, keeping to short simple phrases that repeat will probably be more effective than long sentences, making the words more visceral than heady.)

v) Optional next step: Become them, exploring how they move and breathe. This might seem like an odd thing to do, and unpleasant if you are having a hard time with them, but it can be incredibly powerful, yielding surprising insights. Do they say something? How do they feel towards you? How do they see you? What do they want with or from you?

vi) Write them a letter that you do not have to send. Write it freely, pouring out everything you'd like to say. Then wait a few days and re-read it, making a choice whether to send it, to rewrite and send it, or alternatively just burn it or bury it.

You could do all the above with someone who has died, too. In that case, burning the letter afterwards might be a way of 'sending' it to them, tenderly.

Some years ago, I got a job for a few months doing movement classes with a small group of people who had had strokes. They were all in wheelchairs and severely lopsided, with one side of their body much less active than the other. Their movement would have been the subject of mockery when I was a schoolboy.

During that time, I found their troubled, distorted embodiment showing up in my own practice, as though they'd got inside me somehow. Being with these brave, beautiful humans made a huge impression upon me, and helped me recognise something that was already inside me. They opened the door not only to moving physically in ways that I'd never tried before, but also to depths in my character that are lopsided, strange, even unhinged.

It was such a freedom, and I have never looked back. They got me out of the 'normal' box more radically than any other teacher I've ever had. I have probably thought of them with gratitude more often than any other passers-by in my life.

Practise: Focusing on 'other' (≥10m)

Choose someone to Focus on whom you don't know personally. This could be a politician, a celebrity, or a homeless person on the street. The more 'other' they seem, the more judgements you have, the better.

i) Either use an object to represent them or write their name on a piece of paper. You could even just imagine them there. Place them somewhere in the room.

ii) Warm up for a few minutes until you feel rooted in your body.

iii) Become them. Do their dance until you can feel the resonance within you, feel them as part of you. Let them teach you new ways of being and unlock shadow parts of yourself. You are everything. No exceptions.

iv) Let the part of you that 'is' them write. Let them have a voice.

v) What's the gift here? What aspect of this experience would be valuable to you to have in your daily life?

Focusing on Questions

I'm in a workshop with Marc Silvestre, a trusted colleague and a good friend. He has us all imagine that we're stuck in a box one metre square. We struggle inside it, feeling how trapped we are, and then suddenly he says, 'Break out!'

I burst out of my box and enter into the wildest freedom dance I've done for many years. I am filled with a fiery frenzy, rampaging around the room and shouting, with no idea what exactly it was that I'd just broken free from.

The next day on my way home, I step off a train and without warning I can feel it in my heart: I've made the decision to leave the 5Rhythms world that I've been totally committed to for decades, and create my own practice.

Scared to death and overwhelmed with the magnitude of the task in front of me, I begin to move in that direction. A multitude of new questions await me which I will bring to my practice for years to come, but that first decision is made.

Are you struggling with something, a project, or a decision? During the time I was launching the ZeroOne movement practice, I struggled mightily with all kinds of dilemmas. At the beginning of the process, I was on the fence about whether to do it all. Embodying that question got me started, remarkably, even though I hadn't been aware that I was doing so.

What about you? What are you up against in your life? What are you wrestling with?

Practise: embodying a question (≥10m)

i) Focus your dilemma or struggle into a single question. How simple can you make it? Write down your question or say it aloud. Even if you don't know what the question is, you could call out 'What do I need to see?'

ii) Take a few minutes to warm up physically, getting yourself moving and breathing deeply to get anchored in your body.

iii) Then begin to embody the question, to move as the question. Feel it in your shapes, the way you step around the space, the way you breathe. Say it aloud again and again as you move. Where do you feel it, and how does it show up? Does it propel you backwards or forwards? Is there a pressure in your belly or your chest? How do your arms and hands express your feelings about it? Can you let your head drop into the movement, freeing it from having to come up with an answer?

iv) Rather than grasping for solutions, live the question. Dance, willing not to know.

v) Now, get pen and paper, and write or draw from your experience.

Be patient. Answers may come to you while you move, or they may come later in ways you do not expect. Listen. Stay open-minded and be willing for life to give you your next step in its own good time.

Focusing on Prayer

I am out on the moors at sunrise, longing for God. That's the best way I can put it: longing with all my heart to feel taken by something so much bigger than me that I can do nothing other than let go. With a bumbling mix of movements from my body and sounds from my heart, I allow my dance to call out, reach out, beg for contact.

Sobs racking me open, the longing expands way out beyond 'me' and becomes part of the world, part of creation. I am home again, humbled and holy for a wild moment of grace. It evaporates like morning mist as I cycle home, but the day is warm inside my chest.

As a child at school in the 1970s, morning assemblies mainly consisted of singing hymns and saying prayers that meant nothing to me. I learnt that 'prayer' involves asking an absent father for help with life problems. It felt like empty nonsense.

It was Gabrielle who taught me that prayer can be an act of communion, a two-way exchange. The dance showed me how to become a begging bowl for spirit.

However, later in life, during a time when I hit rock bottom, in sheer desperation I began to pray for help in words again. I found that also invaluable. If I'm engaging with something that is deeply troubling me, or a pattern I feel helpless with, literally asking for help from a higher or deeper power than my personal self does something. It works. Not always in the way I might like, but it works. In fact, it's worked often enough, and I've glimpsed my capacity for trouble often enough, that these days I enter into prayer almost every day both asking for help *and* as communion, not only when I'm desperate.

What you pray to could be Mother Nature, your higher self or the collective intelligence of a support group you're part of. You could call that presence God, Love, or The Force. It could be your family or friendship circle. It also doesn't have to be in words. Just like you can move with a question, you can move with a cry for help or an offering of devotion and gratitude. You can use words at the same time as you move, babble incoherently as you dance, or just let the spirit take your body and breath in holy communion.

Practise: praying for help

Get as clear as you can about what you're asking for help with, what kind of help you're asking for. Say it out loud or write it down, and then dance that prayer. Let the asking fill your body with breath, allowing the desire for help to stream through your blood. Give in to the feelings. Maybe call out the words at the same time. Become the prayer, embodied.

Practise: prayer as communion

Address the higher power you're reaching for by name, whether that's God, Mother Earth, Vast Mystery, Higher Self, or My Family. Call out to that, announcing your presence, and then drop into your dance as deep as you dare. Breathe the longing into your bones and blood. Become that begging bowl for spirit. Let it move through your body.

Focusing Endnotes

Today, it hits me suddenly that I am so tired of 'working on myself'. I mean really... enough is enough. Flopping down on the floor as I begin my practice, I simply don't get up again. Fifteen minutes later, to my surprise, I feel deeply well and nourished by the experience.

Moving with a Focus can make your practice more interesting and turbo-charge the learning process. Once you start, you'll probably find yourself noticing more and more what you need to work with.

For instance, when you're practising Focusing on something, notice your attitude with yourself. Are you firm yet kind, or is there a harshness in you towards yourself? If so, you could take your harshness and explore that through movement, with genuine curiosity rather than trying to get rid of it or change it. Find out what is driving it and what it wants. Where did you learn to be like that with yourself?

I have a friend who keeps a little notebook with her at all times to jot things down as she goes through her day and something triggers her. She then takes it into her practice the next day. Great idea!

However, everything has a shadow side. In the case of Open practice, that's staying within your comfort zones and never challenging yourself. The shadow side of Focused practice is getting fixated on fixing, treating yourself like a psychological engineering project, believing that there's something endlessly wrong with you and you need improving.

Of course, there is some truth in that belief. We are wounded, and our avoidance or denial of the pain creates more pain. We have sore points that need healing, blind spots that need discovering, and there's always a growing edge where we could take a next step and become more wholly ourselves. But it's also true that we are absolute radiant perfection already. Exactly as we are.

Our minds have what's called a 'negativity bias'. We are built to pay more attention to pain or danger than pleasure and wellness. Remember that, and compensate for it by giving time to what delights you. Make space for your joys and loves and gratitudes. Focus on your strengths and pleasures. Enjoy the YES!

Open and Focus modes form the Yin and the Yang of your practice. They can each be undertaken deliberately, as a choice. Next, we'll look at the Surrender mode of practice, which is entirely different. It comes unbidden, as a moment of grace. You cannot force Surrender to happen, but if you dedicate yourself to Open and Focus modes and get strong within both, you'll make yourself more and more available, laying the ground for that grace to come.

10. Surrender

Dance, until you shatter your own self. — Rumi

Your dance is food for the gods
as you let go
part of life
you just let go
break down
break through
with nothing in the way
you fall
and light up from within
utterly alive
intimately surrendered
to the One

Surrender

. . . in which the spirit takes you,
and for a wild moment, you are the dance.

Once you've Surrendered to your dance, even if only for a fleeting moment, you're never quite the same again. You've tasted the nectar of heaven, and you're going to want more. This is the orgasm of movement practice, and it feels amazing.

When you first start to dance as a practice, you try out some moves. It may well be a big deal to move your body in many directions, many shapes, many timbres, beyond the painfully restricted range of physical expression that is normal for most of us, and it probably feels like a big new freedom, at least for a while.

Then the time will come when you find yourself struggling in some way. You may feel excruciatingly vulnerable. An unbidden rage may bubble up within you. Your mind might start clamouring at you to stop and do something else. If you don't dodge the discomfort but stay with it, enter into it, wrestle with it, at some point you will find yourself on an edge where you instinctively know that if you go any further in the same direction, something fundamental is going to change.

Up until now, you've been 'doing' it. With only a moment's warning, the tables have turned and it is doing you. You're being moved, being danced. Something bigger than who-you-thought-yourself-to-be is coming through like a tsunami. You probably could stop it, but you wouldn't dream of doing so because it feels so damn good. The dance sweeps you up in its maw and ecstatically mashes you into a new version of aliveness you never dreamed of. Your body is coursing with wild currents of feeling, your mind is riveted in the present, electric with the moment. Unpredictable and spontaneous, you're not being creative so much as *being the creative spirit*, incarnate.

This is the Flow State that books have been written about. It's The Zone that artists and athletes train for and live for. It might last for a few breaths or long enough that you lose track of time completely. It might leave you broken or whole. It could be overwhelming or gentle. It might be intensely emotional, or it might be subtly Zen. It could be a light refreshment that brings a quiet zing to the rest of your day, or a wild tornado that takes months to integrate and you never really understand.

The point is, you Surrender. You Surrender yourself to something beyond what you identify as 'you' and allow life to take you. You may well resist it for a moment, because the approach usually has an element of discomfort or fear built into the process, but at some point you just let go and let life live itself through you as a dance. You become the dance, and it is a freedom that feels like your birthright.

It is your birthright. Humans have been dancing for a long, long time. Dance is in the matrix of what makes us human. As far as I'm aware, no other species makes music and dances to that music. If ever you doubted whether we deserve a place on this earth, look at that. Aren't we beautiful? We make art, and in the making of it we know ourselves and breathe the divine and become as one with all of creation. For some brief moments, we get out of our heads, expanding beyond the cerebral cortex that is so brilliant and such a bane of our existence, and experience freedom.

All of this is a blessing, literally — it comes by grace, not by command. I've had phases where I'd slip into that zone every time with the first step. I've been through long periods of time when it didn't come at all, and I wondered if I'd lost the capacity for it. Then, without warning, it would take me again, as new and fresh as the first time.

Over the years, for me, the experience of Surrender has changed a great deal. As a young man, it invariably consisted of extremely high energy states and a lot of emotional catharsis, and I would crave it, court it, count on it, feeling bereft if a day's practice went by without a taste of it. That depth of release was something I needed again and again, as it titrated the mountain of distress I'd accumulated whilst growing up. It felt great. A friend joked about my ecstatic relationship with agony, but he was on point. Maybe it was a modern-day version of self-flagellation, but it was more fun than the Christians made it, with plenty of creativity and often some great music backing me up.

Nowadays I'm rarely like that. Mostly, I don't even *want* to get 'high' in that way. Instead, my experience of Surrender has morphed into something more like a gentle whisper, ineffably pleasurable and far more seamlessly integrated into my whole days, not only in moments where I'm officially practising. It has become part of my Zero practice, washing over me when I'm walking down the street or talking with a friend. It comes far more easily than it did when I was young, there as soon as I tune into my body and breath. It's there when I sit still and do nothing. Some things improve with age – which makes up for the knees, to some extent.

Show up regularly for your practice, with dedication and curiosity, and Surrender will come for you.

Especially, don't give up when things are hard and you wish you were somewhere else, doing something else. Don't give up; give in. Give in to whatever is happening for you, allowing it to become your doorway, your next step. At those times, go into the pain, or fear, or boredom, or tiredness, or grief, or rage, or numbness, or cynicism, or nagging thoughts. Take any of these 'problems' and pour them into your movement, turning your suffering into art, as Gabrielle counselled me to do a thousand times.

Nothing is too big, too small, too ugly or too dark for the dance. It can absorb and embrace ANYTHING.

Western culture is afraid of Surrender. It's all geared up to resist it, hanging on instead to control, separation and domination. But life is stronger. The wild uncontrollable dance that has been root and stock of human life on earth is returning, and you can be part of it.

Fear

I'm on a weekend workshop in Oxford led by Susannah and Ya'Acov Darling-Khan. They will later go on to create the Movement Medicine practice, but at this point in 1991, they are nascent, yet already inspired and inspiring, 5Rhythms teachers.

On the second day, dancing across the room to the big-bellied beat of Ya'Acov's African djembe drum, I can sense myself being drawn towards totally letting myself go, and I'm terrified. Alarm bells ring in every cell of my body, telling me that I am about to be destroyed.

Standing right on the edge and looking down into the abyss of my unknowing, by some grace, it suddenly dawns upon me that, far from wanting to destroy me, a Divine presence is holding me so gently in its hands that whatever happens, all will be well.

It's safe to let go.

I step into the void, and fall.

I fall, and cry out, and fall — in love.

If, like me in my early days of exploring movement, you find fear is what comes up when you sense the possibility of letting go and being danced, could you take an interest in that, rather than believing it to be a problem? Could you courageously make space for that fear, and add it into the mix of your dance?

It's natural to feel fear as we fall towards the truth, and that's what Surrender is. If fear comes up for you, go easy. Take it slow, but take it.

One step at a time.

It may seem to you that what's being stirred up is too cavernous, too unpredictable, too dangerous for you to countenance – especially if you're on your own rather than in a group, held by a skilled facilitator.

You may be aware that old childhood traumas are being touched and worry that without some support you may go in over your head. The thing is, Surrender is exactly that – you go in over your head. It's a liquid immersion. That's its nature.

Surrender is a submission to something greater than you, or at least that's how it seems as you approach it. Once you're in it, you realise that the force threatening to overwhelm you actually is you, just a deeper, higher, vaster aspect of your nature than you usually identify with. You realise that you are in fact breathing just fine under water.

Surrendering to your dance will seem like a loss of self as long as you think you know who you are and are attached to being 'someone', committed to being something (e.g. nice) and not other things (e.g. nasty). Surrender takes you beyond being 'someone' to the place where you're everything.

Everything, and nothing.

You have to let go of all those ideas about yourself, but letting go is not something you can 'do'. You can't command it; it has to happen to you. You have to submit.

It's a grace.

However, not all fears are nonsense. If it feels too scary to let go, maybe it would be too much right now. The truth is, when you dance, you're in the wilderness. It's *not* entirely safe – that's partly why it's so healthy – and we're not always ready to jump in. It's your unique inner wilderness, and no one else can explore it for you, so you'll have to learn for yourself.

Talk to someone you trust about the experience you're having and get some support from a professional if you consistently are concerned for your well-being. Check out Appendix II on trauma for more guidance on this if you haven't already.

Then when you come to these moments in your practice, try holding back; see how it feels. What do you learn? Try stepping over the edge and see how that feels. What do you learn? Get to know your limits. Get to know how it feels to go beyond them.

If you're in fear, paradoxically, *that fear itself* could be your gateway to Surrender. This happens when you allow the fear to be felt, allow it to breathe and move through your body. You dance right into the fear and let the fear dance right through you. At some point your life-force takes over, and that's it – you're through, into the unkempt grace of Surrender. You're no longer 'doing' it – the dance has taken you.

But you can't rush all this. You can't be goal-oriented about it. Surrender is a Zen Koan; you have to give up your goals to get there, but you can't give them up in a 'doing' way. If you're attached to outcomes, you are attached to outcomes. If the truth is that you're striving for Surrender, you'll have to allow that too, because you can't argue with the truth. Rather, become that attachment, your striving, totally, finding its dance. Let your attachment have its way with your whole body, and *that attachment itself* can become your gateway to letting go.

If frustration is there, *become the frustration*, passionately.

If you feel stuck, *become the stuckness*, brilliantly.

If you're numb, empty, or lost, enter right into those places and *find the way you move there*, embodying totally whatever it is that you are in this moment. That way, surrender may come to you.

As Vincent Martínez-Grieco, founder of Soul Motion, said so brilliantly, 'Dance ugly and drool...'

Practise: Surrendering

I cannot give you a specific practice for Surrender. It will come when it comes.

Prepare the ground with dedicated Open and Focus practice, be willing to stay with any levels of energy that are stronger than you're used to, particularly any discomfort, and to be moved in ways that seem strange.

Don't make it too much of a big deal.

Stay with yourself as things return to normal.

Surrendering Endnotes

How are your resources? Do you have people you can reach out to should you find yourself stirred up by an experience that you cannot integrate or make sense of, leaving you destabilised for too long and making it hard for you to function in the world? Do you have both friends and professionals, should you need them?

Do you know how to ground yourself and calm your nervous system, at least to some extent, when you need to? If not, re-read the *Calming, Grounding, Resting* section in *Basics* (Chapter 6) and include those practices in your days and weeks.

You may also want to find a body-oriented psychotherapist or bodyworker, or someone skilled in working with altered states of consciousness. Just as the Open and Focus modes of practice have their shadow side, so does Surrender. It can be addictive, even destructive, especially if you prize it above all other modes, don't know how to stay grounded through it, or don't give time to integrating the experience into the rest of your life.

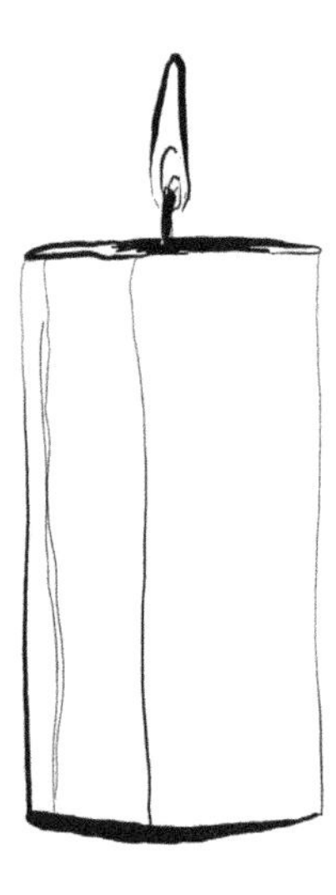

Here are my top suggestions on how to keep your practice healthy, allowing moments of Surrender to come and go without it being a big deal.

- Stay aware of your physical body throughout, *not just the energy coursing through it*. Notice it's weight, shape, movement patterns. Practise valuing the physical in the ordinary times, so that when you're high, that way of being down to earth is natural and instinctive to you.

- When you find yourself in a strong experience of Surrender, stay on track as you 'come down'. Don't cut away abruptly, but give time for things to complete whilst staying present with yourself, especially physically. Taking time to rest is healthy.
- If you find yourself releasing a lot of strong emotions, you may find it helpful to write about the experience afterwards. You could journal what came up for you, or perhaps more appositely, write a poem about it. If drawing or painting is your thing, do that.
- If you're very stirred up, it can be tempting to engage in more catharsis in order to release the feelings. However, it may serve you better to move slowly, carefully, pausing often or even just resting, gently staying present with your body. If even that stirs you up more, you could try being restful whilst paying attention to something else that's beautiful, like something in nature, or music that you love. There's value in calming down.

Many people would disagree with me here, but I think stability, safety and functionality are overrated in our culture. There's a place for overwhelm, extreme states of consciousness, and taking risks with yourself. There's great resilience to be found by jumping into the unknown without holding back and finding out who you are there.

Yes, it may cause ripples that leave you relatively unable to proceed as normal for a while. But how important is it to you, really, to be consistently 'normal'? If you're adventurous, intense practice could at times create such big waves within you that it's difficult to function in the world for a few hours, days or even longer. You decide: what do you value? What are you living for?

Opening up to the deepest aspects of your nature is not entirely safe. That doesn't necessarily mean you should avoid it. Life isn't safe. It's your path, your life, and your vulnerability on the line. You may not have the same relationship to risk as I do. I like the edge when I'm walking in high mountains, and I like the edge inside myself too. If risk is not your thing, then take it slow. You can let go gently, a little bit at a time.

Building resilience step by step, becoming familiar with the different states that movement can take you to, you'll find that you can trust your feet more and more, loving what happens when you relinquish control and Surrender to the wild creative spirit that is your deepest YOU.

11. Give

If you want happiness for an hour, take a nap. If you want happiness
for a day, go fishing. If you want happiness for a year, inherit a
fortune. If you want happiness for a lifetime, help someone else.
— Chinese proverb

Today, the street corner is my dance floor, subtle slow samba I turn
on the bakery is a delightful speed date as she hands me a croissant,
eyes meeting, never to be seen again the woods are a church that
pierces my armour and blesses my brokenness in an intimate damp
evening mist

washing up gets hip when Bob Marley's calling in writing an email
warms up when I lean back and stretch out, wriggling through my
frustration stuck in traffic is almost fun when I let out a yell from
time to time, resetting my rush-hour to Zero

hugging my mother has never been the same, since I danced that
baby's loss speaking with Dad, since I found his gait in mine
playing with the kids, since I remembered to jump for joy

standing waiting, scrolling my phone with the crowd
I stop, shift my weight, look up beyond the horizon,
sense my aching body and let out a sigh

I hear the cry of the world, and know I am responsible
for the one tiny piece of it that is receiving the imprint of this breath
right now
— what can I Give You, dear One?

How can I be of service, today?

. . . in which you take what you've found on the dance floor and Give it freely to a world that is longing for you.

Open, Focus, and Surrender all happen 'on the dance floor'. You're in dedicated time, whether it's a moment or many hours, where movement is your meditation.

Give happens everywhere else.

Dance connects us to our most authentic, vibrant, creative self, aligning us with the essential vitality and mystery of the life force we're animated by. We become breath made visible in form and motion: we literally become inspiration.

How about sharing some of that good stuff around??

It is not enough to merely do your own solo practice. Maybe at some points in your life the hermit archetype is genuinely the thing, but the human race is in massive transition, and if ever there was a time for calling 'All hands on deck!' as Clarissa Pinkola Estes has put it, this must be it.

How can you play your whole and holiest part if you only practice alone, if you consider your practice to be something that only happens for twenty minutes in the morning before the kids get up, separate from the rest of your life?

Once you get into it, the Give mode is by far the biggest chunk of your practice. In terms of hours in the day, the opportunities far outweigh what you do in Open, Focus, or Surrender. But also, the options for how you practise Giving are endless. The brief ideas I'm offering you here are a starting point.

Why Give?

Back in the days when I was still teaching the 5Rhythms, I was subbing for a class at a college in London. To get into the building, we had to sign in at a security desk by the front door. A friend of mine came along who'd never been to that class before and told me that before she could say a word to the security guy, he had taken one look at her and said, '5Rhythms?'

'Yes, how did you know?'

'Well, you looked me straight in the eyes like you were really seeing me, and smiled.'

There's a whole world out there, and the majority of its humans are not getting down and juicy with themselves all that often. Most of us, most of the time – on the street, at work, at home – are stuck in our heads, far from being the freedom-seeking, openly loving, unique creatives that we're born to be.

Most of us, most of the time, are quietly desperate, constantly monitoring ourselves to act normal, hoping that the strange maverick we know ourselves to be deep down is not revealed and reviled. As young children, there's an innate drive to connect authentically with others, bubbling enthusiastically through our embodiment and expression. Tragically, painfully, we generally have this delight trained out of us, forcing us into the straight and narrow – physically, emotionally, mentally, creatively – nipping any possibility of creativity in the bud.

Yet aren't we all aching to be found out? To be noticed by warm eyes and touched by a loving hand? We live so many of our precious moments caught, freeze frame, between hoping to be seen and fearing the reaction we'd get if we were.

One of the wonderful things that can happen when we dance is that we break through all that self-management stuff and just show up, for real, with each other. When everybody's weirdness is visible, it's not such a big deal.

How about experimenting with stretching those social norms while you're out there in the world? Sharing a little of the aliveness you find in your practice when you're on the street?

That's Give: scoop up the inspiration you get from all those beads of sweat you've laid out on the dance floor and share it with the world as it shows up in front of you.

Generously.

When we dance, we become more —

- *Embodied:* We are inhabiting these bones, blood and breath to a depth and fullness that is remarkable by mainstream human standards.
- *Wholehearted:* Moving the whole body whilst breathing consciously, our feelings will soon come up and out.
- *Honest:* It cannot be any other way. The body doesn't lie.
- *Creative:* When you don't know what steps to take, you make them up on the spot. You are three-dimensional spontaneous art in motion.
- *Prayerful:* Fundamentally, dance is meditation, presence, and prayer.

Let's look at each of these qualities, and how we might Give something to the world through them.

Embodiment

To be embodied in public is radical, nonviolent, direct action because the collective agreement to be *dis*embodied and constrained is so very strong.

I manage it some of the time. Occasionally, I might dance in an unlikely place, but there are many more subtle ways to be embodied than that. I allow myself to be more mobile than average. I walk more freely than is the English way. If I'm in a queue, instead of standing obediently still, I might stretch when I need to, or shift my weight around in a slow foot dance. Simple stuff like that.

But even if nothing is visible, when I feel more private or shy, I can stand in that queue practising a deep level of embodied consciousness, and I'm sure the atmosphere around me is changed somehow, which affects everyone. We humans are incredibly sensitive to each other, and anyone doing anything by conscious choice becomes a catalyst for others to follow.

You don't have to be 'in public', though.

Doing the dishes? Notice your body. Adjust anything that isn't quite right. Want some music on? Enjoy!

Digging the weeds? Notice your body. Maybe you'll have an impulse to pause and gaze at the sky for a moment that you might otherwise have ignored.

Having a conversation with your mother? Your boss? The kids? Notice your body. Do you have the impulse to change anything? Lean in a little closer, or back off a bit? Relax your shoulders, or sit up straighter? How's your jaw? Need a deep breath? How about putting your feet more firmly on the ground?

When you make these adjustments, do any of them change your emotional tone, or your perception? I find that when I'm aware of my body in conversation, I'll often have the impulse to move either closer or further away than is the custom. I'll reach out and touch a hand or put my arm round a shoulder, more often than is the default of my upbringing or my culture. Other times I may need to strengthen boundaries, speaking with someone from a little further away than I usually would.

These little things can create a healthier, happier way of moving in the world. Small, ordinary steps, over and over again. No rush. No big expectations.

Listen for physical sensations, impulses to change position, move, pause, or deepen the breath. Simple things.

Listen to your body.

Practise: walking

Walk down the street with the aliveness of a dancer. Keep it subtle; you're not trying to get attention, but deepen your presence. Be aware of your body and enjoy that. Breathe fully. Look around you rather than down. Be part of the world, physically.

Practise: relating

In conversation with someone, whether friend or foe, listen to your body. How are you feeling with that person? Tense? Energised? Warm or cold?

Do you need to move closer or further away?

Change posture?

Touch?

Wholeheartedness

I grew up in a typically English emotional desert, and for a child who had gaping wounds from his early years, that was truly ghastly. The combination of deep, titanic emotional currents and the imperative to not show anything outwardly created severe twists in my gut, heart, and mind.

For this reason, it was an incredible discovery of freedom to learn to use my body to express my feelings, to totally letting rip with no concern about being 'too much'. As a result, I'm passionate about being wholehearted.

Living in England as I do, I am surrounded by a culture that still often echoes that agonising childhood twist: act normal, even when you're feeling a lot. But whilst England might be towards the end of the 'withheld' spectrum, we're not so unusual. What's it like where you are? Are some feelings more taboo than others?

True, light, generous joy is often met with deep suspicion where I live, whereas tight-lipped repressed anger is so common it's easy not to notice it unless one's been away for a while. Sadness is difficult for many people I've met in the USA. Fear has a bad rap everywhere.

What are you surrounded by?

Notice who you're with a bit more keenly than usual. What space are they in right now? Can you tell? What do you sense? How could you lean into the habits of 'normal' in such a way as to stretch things a bit? Could you be boldly open-hearted enough to open new pathways between you, but not so much that it's intolerable?

You're looking to light up the situation with a glow, not an eruption. Unless, of course, you want to create a revolution – there's a time and a place for everything – but if you're going to deliberately blow fuses and your deep-down intent is to make the world a better place, you'd better be ready to deal with the consequences of your actions. If you've just crashed through someone's boundaries, how could you follow through in a healthy way? Are you willing to stay in relationship while they integrate the experience? Otherwise, you're doing little more than taking a dump in public.

Practice: with a stranger

Next time you're out shopping, make eye contact with someone a bit more deeply than normal. Slip into the consciousness of a dancer and notice who you're looking at. Can you see any receptivity to connection there? (If not, maybe take the cue and let it go.)

Who is that in front of you? Can you find a way to be a little more heartfelt than normal? Smile? Say something true? Ask them something respectful but personal?

How could you love?

Practice: with a loved one

Spending time with someone dear to you, in peace, conflict, or ordinariness, could you slip into the consciousness of a dancer and notice who you're looking at with fresh eyes?

Could you find a way to be a little more wholehearted than is the norm for you both?

If you listen to their presence using your own body, what do you sense about their state of being in this moment?

Can you let your feelings show through your body, your face, your eyes, your tone of voice?

Honesty

The body tells the truth. The way you stand, move and breathe speaks volumes about you. When we dance, our feelings, thoughts and actions sync up to create a unified whole, and our essential nature shines through. We radiate our individuality. There's a whole and holy honesty about that, which can feel incredibly liberating and healthy. Finding ways to carry this vulnerable openness into ordinary moments can turn a life around. (It did mine, so I know what I'm talking about, not least because it took me many years before I got the lesson. I learned the hard way.)

Off the practice floor, radical and revelatory honesty is not always the best policy though. It depends on who you're with and what's going on. If you open yourself up to be seen in a context where you will not be appreciated for it, that can be a kind of self-abuse. There's value in learning to be invisible, holding your cards close to your chest if you sense you may not be respected. However, the intricate duplicity and manipulations that often pass for 'being sociable' seldom serve or satisfy anyone.

You can at least practise being honest with yourself. Notice what is going on for you – what you feel, think, fear and desire in any given moment.

Then, you can practise boldly or carefully revealing what's true for you, especially in the relationships you treasure.

Speaking the truth in ways that can be heard, at the right moment, is an art. You'll know when you get it right by sensing the atmosphere as you speak and immediately afterwards – the truth always makes you feel lighter. It's a relief, in some way, even if it's hard to say or to hear.

What if there's someone you like, but you've got into a rut of hanging out in ways that don't feel good to you deep down? Maybe there's a fear of silence between you — how then would it be to ask, 'Can we walk in silence for a moment?' And then some time later, 'How was that?'

If a conversation stalls, you could tell someone how you feel, more directly than is socially normal.

If you get bored, you could dare to tell someone that you're drifting away, not fully paying attention, and wondering why.

If you're curious about something, you could ask a question that's more personal than you're used to.

Speaking the truth can be challenging, but if it's love you're seeking, there's no avoiding it. I've found that for me, a vital step if I'm going to reveal something that's scary for some reason is to preface it with a kind of introduction, that might go something like this: 'I need to say something to you, and I'm scared of... [fill in the blank] happening if I tell you. Would you please hear me, and then be honest with me in return? I'd genuinely like to hear your response. I'm doing this with the intention of us knowing each other better, because I care about our relationship.' That way, you're asking their help to break through something, being clear about your reasons for doing so, and leading with your vulnerability. This is very different from ploughing in unannounced and blurting it out.

Another key I've found is to give space for feelings. Often, deepening a relationship with a moment of truth-telling can bring up strong emotional responses for one or both of you. If you notice that's happening, either for you as the speaker or for the one who's listening, try acknowledging that, making space for it. You could say, 'I can see you're feeling a lot right now. Am I right? I don't want to ride rough-shod over that. I haven't finished what I was saying, but if I pause, would you tell me what's happening?'

You'll have to improvise and find the right words of course, because to do this well — to engage skilfully with someone in deepening truth — is a dance, and you'd better treat it as such, engaging what you've learnt in your practice about listening *at the same time as expressing yourself*. You do that in your solo practice, listening to the calls and impulses of your body, and maybe music too, at the same time as creating moves that express those impulses or embody the music. With practice, it can become seamless, instinctive.

This is the key to Giving honestly: to reveal the truth in a way that it can be received, you have to *listen while you speak*. Listen to your body, listen to the feeling-tone of whom you're talking to, and listen to the atmosphere in the room. Then speak responsively and with kindness, as a gift to all that you are hearing.

Practise: listening for what's true

In a relationship that's important to you and that you'd like to deepen, approach it as a dance, listening for the truth of what's going on for you and between the two of you. Is there something you could reveal about yourself, or the dynamic between you, even if it's something you might usually hide?

In the process of opening up, notice if you're scared, and consider revealing that first.

In the times when you're speaking, can you listen with your body to the person you're with? What can you sense about them? Can you be responsive to that, adapting the flow of what you're saying to match?

Grounded in that sensitivity to the other, what would come if you completed the sentence, 'The truth is...' ?

Creativity

We're all born artists. Some more keenly than others, for sure, but the idea that art is only for the great ones, and that there's a standard of talent below which you'd better not try — that's soul-torture. It's a terrible mistake, causing mass chronic depression and hopelessness.

From far, far back in the distant past, human beings have danced wild, sung songs, told stories. Everyone: old, young, infirm and all. We have danced all together to let go of demons and celebrate aliveness. We have sung while tilling the fields. We have told stories around the fire to weave our dreams into the fabric of the village.

Creativity is not only singing songs or painting pictures, though. And singing songs or painting pictures is not always done creatively. You can sweep a floor or walk down the street with a subtle creative flair about you. Many people express their creativity through the way they tend a garden, bring up children, or build a business. You can even take a breath creatively, because it's not about creating 'something'. It's about an attitude, a mode of perception, a way of being that has nothing to do with a particular activity.

To live creatively is not something I've been able to force. It's not something I have mastered; it is more like ongoing humbling work in progress. In fact, any thoughts such as 'I've got this now' inevitably lead to a fall that brings me back to earth with a grief that washes away such arrogance and renders me capable of creating from a more innocent place again.

Isn't it like that for all of us? I think so. There are no guarantees; to stay creative is to be vulnerable, imperfect, human.

A good practice session will get you 'in the zone', in a Flow-State. There's an integrated quality about you, with mind, heart and body all functioning as aspects of a Self that is courageous, aware, spontaneous, loving, and uniquely creative. To live this way involves listening to the moment and responding to it freely. There's a joyfulness, gratitude and appreciation about it that is independent of whether you like what's going on or not. Even if you're scared, angry or sad, that lightness can be there.

Creativity is our nature, and like the rest of nature, it has cycles. There are times when we'll feel totally switched on and happening, with a lot of creative output. Then there'll be fallow periods, down-times when it seems like nothing much is going on. But it is: it's just that the creative spirit has become subtle, more like a quiet way of moving through our days. Sometimes a depression might come, and we wonder if we've lost it for good, but it's only the creative winter, when it's as well to be restful and allow our dreams to go underground for a while. We can long for the spring to return, but there's no need to push. Come it will. Until it does, we can use our practice to grieve, allowing any depression to become a slow-moving sadness, surrendering to the downward movement and the heaviness.

Anything that you 'make' is an offering to the world, whether it's a dance or a dinner, a chant or a child, or just a lilt in your step on the street. It's a piece of your light, shining out there. And it's light even if it's 'dark' – plenty of inspiration can come from painful places and be turned into a creative offering. It's still you lighting up the world, even if the colour is a deep grey-blue. We Give what we can.

Is there anything you're longing to Give, that way? Do you paint, write, sing? Is there a way that your creativity could come out that's not a 'performance' or a career choice but a natural sharing of 'you'?

Practise: ordinary creativity

You're engaged in an ordinary activity such as doing the dishes or walking down the street. How could you do so with a creative spirit, so there's nothing unusual in your actions, but it feels different? As you're doing that ordinary thing, become the way you are when you dance, just through your state of consciousness. That's it.

Practise: art-based creativity

Is there an art form you'd love to experiment with that you haven't tried before?

Could you try it with no concern for whether it looks good, or measures up to anyone else's standards? How could you create out of curiosity and the playfulness of trying something new?

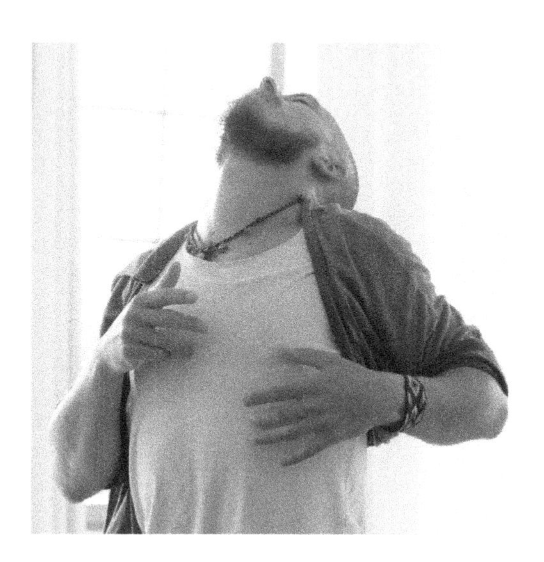

Prayer

We've been looking at ways to Give that are off the dance floor, outside of your movement practice. But there is a way to Give *during* your practice, which might be called prayer. I believe this is always happening on a subtle level, but adding your conscious intent would strengthen and deepen its potency.

Tibetan monks who spend their lives in meditation, far from the everyday world, believe they are nevertheless contributing to humanity by opening up pathways to a deeper or more expanded consciousness, making it easier for the rest of us to get there. I reckon they're onto something. Likewise, many of the original peoples of the Americas recognise the interrelatedness of all, meaning that they're praying not only for themselves but their family, all people, and the rest of creation too.

We exist in a matrix of life, with everything moved by everything else. When you enter your practice, you could do so with that awareness, consciously dedicating yourself to all of life. That way, it becomes a Give experience, and not only for your self-improvement agenda. It's generous, and it's a pleasure to feel connected in that way. It's a blessing to be able to Give something.

Practise: prayer

At the start of a movement session, find some way to acknowledge that the inner work you are about to undertake is for the benefit of all. You might speak aloud to your sense of higher power, or you might say 'May this dance be one for all'.

At the end, you might give thanks for being able to contribute something with your practice.

Give Endnotes

I'm about to eat a delicious healthy lunch that I've prepared for myself. I sit down, intending to eat consciously, Giving to myself as a practice. It has to be that deliberate, otherwise I'd probably stick on a podcast I've been wanting to listen to and eat too fast without noticing much.

Before I even take a bite, I tune in to my body and can feel the panic. It's subtle, but I know it well enough to recognise the deep underground tremor in my cells, easily triggered by receiving nourishment. This fear has been with me all my life. I attend to it as best I can, wrapping my arms around my chest and shoulders, rocking back and forth, allowing the distress and pain that's woven in with the fear to move through and integrate, becoming compassion. A deep grief wells up for all the years of background torment I've lived, for what I went through to create it, so early on.

It's a while before I can eat, but when I do, slowly, a deep peace spreads throughout my body. I lie down afterwards, glowing gently, savouring the experience.

All of the Give actions involving other people are moment to moment, courageous, creative acts of engagement that could fall completely flat (especially if you have strong expectations) or land you in hot water with someone. They all break the mould of normal, and that can be challenging for those around you. Some people will welcome the opening, some will resist and push back.

Watch out for what's driving you — is it truly an openly generous sharing of the inspiration and life-fullness you found through movement, with no attachment to outcome? Or is it laced with rebellious criticism and judgement towards conventionality and normalcy? If it's the latter, that's going to come back at you.

This needn't be a recipe for hesitant trepidation — you could bravely go for it, and as with all the other practice modes, you'll learn about yourself. What you Give will come back reflected, with some aspects amplified. Take the hints. Notice what goes on, how you feel, how you're received, what you see.

I've learnt a lot about my anger this way — anger that was so taboo as a child that I learnt to stash it, stuff it, dress it up in polite clothing, and pretend to myself that it didn't exist. Over and over again, when I think I'm being generously embodied, passionate, honest and creative in the way I relate to people, I notice (often too late) a subtle aggression in my behaviour that wasn't generous at all. I can be harsh and pushy, tainted by unconscious judgements of the person I see in front of me. That stuff is a major blindspot for me. I'm getting better at it, mostly thanks to Maria-Carin, who now sees it a mile off, but it's slow work in progress.

Practise: giving beauty

Find a single flower, whether from a florist or your garden. Walk down a busy street with your intuition scanning for the 'right' person, and then trust the impulse: give them the flower whilst staying receptive and responsive to their experience. Maybe you say something, maybe you don't.

Afterwards, as you walk away: what did you learn about yourself? How do you feel now?

Sometimes, the one to Give to is yourself, grounding your practice in simple things like the way you eat, or the way you shower. Both of those examples have been strong ones for me, as in the example above. By default, I feed myself in the way an impatient parent might do with a toddler, shoving food in as fast as possible, oblivious to my body's natural pace or even the pleasure of eating. Likewise, while showering, I would wash myself quite roughly, coldly practical, getting it over with quickly as though it's a chore. It was a shock to see both those patterns, and it saddened me to reflect on how I presumably learnt to be that way with my body.

It still takes a conscious choice to do things differently — to eat without rushing, paying attention and savouring not only the taste but the entire experience, and to wash myself with a loving touch, tenderly. When I do though, my whole nervous system calms down a notch or two from the constant underlying state of panic I have lived with for most of my life.

Writing about this now, I can feel whispers of the shame that's so deeply imprinted in me around being loving to myself. Maybe it's partly a man-thing, too. The cultural imprinting I grew up in categorically stated that, as a man, I should have a relationship with my body that's tough, not tender. Like all core wounds, it's ongoing work in progress.

All too often, the state of nervous system arousal that passes for 'normal' gets to hold the steering wheel, and I rush through a meal anyway, even though I know what's happening. It seems I can't be bothered to care for myself. There's that deeply buried anger again, manifesting as impatience towards myself and the business of living.

I relate this very personal struggle to illustrate the nature of Give practice. It brings stuff up, as the other modes do. It brings you face to face with yourself. To include this practice mode in your life asks a lot of you, as any decent practice does: persistence, dedication, creativity, courage, curiosity, compassion, and more. It requires a willingness to pick yourself up when you fall, dust yourself off, and begin again.

The shadow side of Give can be a self-conscious and self-important sense of 'Now I'm doing my Give practice'. I can be that way sometimes, subtly proselytising to anyone I meet. Ugh.

If you're taking yourself a little too seriously, maybe back off and question your agendas. Practice Open and Focus consistently, Surrender when it comes, then at best, Give will be an effortless overflowing of your movement practice, needing only a moment of awareness in order to jump through the Castaneda-esque windows of opportunity that life will continually bring up right in front of you.

That way, it can be easy, playful, experimental and deep-down-joyful, adding meaning and purpose to your whole Pathway Home, because it's no longer all about you.

So, your practice can take any of these forms – Open, Focus, Surrender or Give. But there is that central element too, the one that, although we have left it till last, is the core of your practice. It is the spirit that breathes through every moment, the fulcrum it all revolves around. It's just that you might not notice it for a long time, as I didn't. But like me, you might look back years later to finally see what had been there all along.

This is: *Zero.*

12. Zero

Stop fighting the system.
The new liberation is the silence inside you.
— Alex Serra

zero is not a circle

but the space inside

if you look into the space

there is nothing to focus... on...

0

no-thing

when you see the no-thingness there
what happens inside you?
what can you touch within YOU
that is no-thing?

the silence underneath your thinking
the stillness behind your heartbeat
the spaciousness within without your body

utterly open
as empty space, silence and stillness
in this way:

physically, we are sexual energy with no desired agendas
emotionally, we are love with no conditional others
mindfully, we are awareness with no thoughts attached
wholly, holy, we are One

• Zero

. . . in which there is only now, and this, and us.

Movement is life, and our bodies are full of it. But there's something else about our nature that doesn't move. It is not the body, not feelings, not thoughts. It is a presence, a consciousness, a something that we experience as totally still. It's a silent spaciousness, a presence that is within every moment of your life whether you're aware of it or not. I sometimes call it Zero.

I described the art of Surrender as a Zen Koan; being present within Zero is another one. Everything we're ordinarily aware of has some kind of form the mind can latch on to, but Zero doesn't. We can't grasp it, yet we can experience it. To paraphrase the extraordinary shaman Lujan Matus, 'We can learn to pay attention to that which cannot be seen, listen to that which cannot be heard, feel that which cannot be touched.'

There's a lot of emphasis in current meditation culture on mindful experience, but when we sense into the silent, still, spaciousness that all mystics speak of, it's not just in the mind, but also a heartful experience. If we're deeply embodied, being in Zero is a deliciously sexual experience too, though far beyond any stereotype we might have around what 'sexual' is.

Being in Zero meditation can be the devotional core of your practice that is always with you, whether you're dancing, in a business meeting, or first opening your eyes in the morning. I say devotional because although that presence itself appears to have no quality about it other than a kind of 'is-ness', the experience of it is so profoundly pleasurable, so full of wellness, that we naturally love it. Being with that presence evokes our loving, our delight in life. Our devotion.

For me, over the years — while I've often been more conscious of wrangling with my suffering, bringing up my kids, learning the craft of my work — there's been a slow growth of my sense of Zero. It has been invisible to me much of the time, but in the long view, I can see it. It's as though I've been tending a garden diligently for all these years, paying attention to the business of pulling weeds, laying compost, planting seeds, and without my noticing, the soil itself has slowly changed, going from a stony wasteland to a lush, deep brown, fertile base that can support life beautifully.

I've learnt dozens of techniques, dealt with countless emotional tsunamis, brought troubled relationship issues into my practice in the hope of happiness or at least relief, wrestled with dysfunctional beliefs, danced through life-path choices. You name it — I've probably done it. Beyond any of that self-management though, the embodied presence of Zero has my devoted attention, growing quietly through all my travails and effortful journeying.

Zero is in essence unexplainable, unintelligible, unknowable, which makes it impossible to write about accurately, but I'm going to try. Please forgive the inevitable falling short.

When we open to Zero, it is *directly experienced* in four distinct ways:

- *Physically*: Through the body, we experience the presence of Zero as a subtle hum of aliveness which is our sexual energy, a constant flow of life recreating itself. Every moment, your body is a veritable fountain of life, untold trillions of cells busy regenerating themselves. Every moment, your breath is making love with your body, in and out, in and out, in and out. This is sexuality as utterly open contentless energy, nothing to do with 'having sex'. It is a total immersion in the riotous, self-organising chaos that is life.

- *Emotionally*: Through the heart, we experience Zero as love – love as utterly open contentless bliss, with no object attached. This open love is a space of ruthless compassion through which any feeling is free to flow – fear, anger, sadness, joy and all their nuanced variations can pass through like the weather – but the quality of love is untouched by any of it, remaining totally open and spacious.
- *Mindfully*: Through the mind, we experience Zero as utterly open contentless awareness, beyond or behind or inside any thinking. Thoughts come of course, but the fundamental quality of consciousness itself is the space within which they arise, pass through and disappear, leaving that awareness unmoved.
- *Wholly*: With body, heart and mind as a unified field of 'I am', we experience Zero as including all, inside and out, both context and centre point. It is both the formless matrix within which all of creation happens and the presence found at the core of all things. Everything is alive, and more than connected: truly One.

All four of these ways of experiencing Zero have a quality of stillness, silence and spaciousness, and at the same time an ineffable sense of being not only connected to the source, but of being that source. Like, 'Ohmygod, that's actually me!' But there is no 'me', at least not in any sense of *being* separate from anything else.

Because this is true, and because truth is beautiful, and because beauty is a pleasure, the experience of being in Zero is a delight.

Let's look at how you might find what's already there.

In Practice

I'm walking an ancient pathway in the Ardèche region of France. I am aware of the countless others who have walked this way before me. I am one of many, part of a long group, strung out over centuries.

The sun is hot and the rocks of the path are golden, worn, dry. There's a silent stillness in the air, no one else around other than these echoes from the past. I fall into an easy rhythm with my feet and breath, and the silence is inside me too. I am a timeless pilgrim, and it is bliss to walk with no destination. I am just walking, for the sake of being alive on earth along with the whole of creation. I am filled with the space that my footsteps delight in.

You do not have to be sitting on a Zen cushion to be in Zero.

You can be cooking dinner, digging the garden, walking the dog. You can be lying in bed on your way to falling asleep. You can even be using a laptop. (That one's a challenge, though!)

These days, you can learn how to meditate through most information channels on the planet, but in case you've never tried it and would like some pointers, here's one way that I would suggest:

Practise: being in Zero (≥5m)

Decide how much time you have for your practice, and divide it in two.

For the first half, move your body. With or without music, get your bones moving, blood flowing, breath deepening.

Then for the second half, drop the movement and be still in a relaxed, comfortable posture, with your eyes closed. You can sit on the floor or a chair, or you can even lie down.

During this second half, being still, lightly widen your attention out until it is completely open and you're simply resting as awareness. Breath comes and goes. Sensations, feelings, thoughts come and go. No problem. You stay resting as awareness and allow whatever comes to come... and go.

Listen to the silence

Be the stillness

Open into the spaciousness

Zero is nowhere no where now here

Practise this regularly and repeatedly, and you will begin to feel some familiarity with it.

Once you've got a sense of this no-thingness, here's the gold: *while you're moving*, sense the stillness within each movement. Listen for the silence within your breath. Become the spaciousness that is Zero.

In this way, you integrate the two halves of the above practice into one whole. Zero is inside everything, *and* it is the field within which everything happens. It's actually impossible not to be completely immersed in it. It is you.

How do you sense it most keenly? As a subtle hum of aliveness in every cell of your body? As a wide-open love radiating from your heart? As a field of awareness within which you experience everything? As a flow-state, from which you generate a constant creative connection to the world around you? Maybe all of the above?

You can practice this 24/7, irrespective of whatever activity you're engaged in.

You can get timers on your phone that ring with Tibetan bells or other sounds that are sweeter than electronic beeps. I have one setting that rings a bell every seven minutes. Some days I switch that on, so throughout the day I am reminded to be a dance, right now.

It's not about suddenly breaking out into wild moves whilst buying broccoli or writing an email though; it's about noticing my body, my breath. Meditation, like dancing, is an attitude. It's about becoming present as an embodied experience. The timer is actually going off right now as I'm writing: I pause for a breath, stretch, look up from the laptop, check in with my body.

Without that timer I can go for vast stretches of time without fully noticing, especially when looking at a screen. There is a background awareness of my body and breath that I have from all the years of practice I'e put in, but the timer helps make it more conscious. It's a relatively new part of my practice, and I'm excited about it, anticipating that it will have an effect of ingraining that kind of micro-practice in myself more firmly, making it more habitual.

Doing the dishes, digging the weeds, driving the car, watching the sun set. Listening to morning birdsong. Fighting or loving.

Zero. A lifetime's work, to begin again today.

Now.

(Yes... *now*... take a breath... be attentive... relax... feel... open...)

13: Obstacles to Practice

Loving God will probably bring you close to him in twenty years, but hating God will get you there in two. — Robert Bly

So, how about all those obstacles to practising? The 'but', the fears, the doubts and limitations. The lack of motivation.

I've been talking to people for decades about this, and before writing this section I asked on Facebook, 'What stops you practising movement at home?' It was a fascinating and, at times, very touching thread, with more comments than I've ever had for any post. Quite a few people gaily wrote 'Nothing!', but there were many others whose answers coalesced into specific categories, so I've pulled them together here to look at.

There's one thing they all have in common though, one obstacle that sums up all the divergent nuances we come up against: *our thinking.*

The old adage of 'Don't believe everything you think' can come in handy here. These are the main thoughts I've noticed:

Thought #1: 'I don't have enough space/time'

Thought #2: 'I don't have the right music'

Thought #3: 'I don't have the discipline'

Thought #4: 'My experience should be similar to what I've become used to in a class, and it isn't, so something's wrong'

Thought #5: 'I would miss the group energy' or 'I miss the contact with other people'

Thought #6: 'I don't believe it would be useful' or 'I couldn't do it properly'

Thought #7: 'I'm scared of what might happen, especially of strong feelings coming up and being alone with that'

Thought #8: 'I don't value myself enough to do it'

Thought #9: 'My neighbours would be disturbed' or 'I don't have any privacy', or 'the kids are always around'

Thought #10: 'I'm too distracted by daily life'

Thought #11: 'I'm too self-conscious – it would feel weird'

Thought #12: 'I need structure and don't know how to create it'

Some of these can be overcome, such as not having the right music, while others you may be stuck with, such as a noisy floor with sensitive neighbours downstairs. None of them need stop you though. You might just have to open your mind and get creative. A lot of them can be surmounted by dropping your expectations. Look at #4 for instance: the expectation that your experience should be similar to being in a class. When you let go of that, all kinds of options open up.

What would it take to drop that expectation? What if you don't try to emulate the experience of being in a class at all, but simply make a space in your day to drop into embodiment, being open to whatever happens?

If you stick with it, your Pathway Home is a kind of pilgrimage, meandering through many landscapes over the years, leading to the same destination of all long, long journeys: being at home within yourself.

Difficulties with practice are a bit like getting a stone in your shoe. The first thought usually goes something like, 'This is a problem; I have to stop what I was doing (journeying) and deal with it.' So we stop to take the stone out of our shoe, believing that once we get rid of it we can keep going the way we were.

But your Pathway Home is a magical one. That stone in your shoe, if you give it your devoted attention, can become a portal. Rather than taking it out of your shoe and throwing it away, be curious about your 'problem'. Rather than dealing with the difficulty briskly so that you can get on with business as usual, take it into your practice, where it can open out into a whole new part of yourself. What you thought was an obstacle to overcome turns out to be a threshold, inviting you into a new relationship with yourself and your practice.

What's in the way IS the way.

In my mid-forties I fell off a ladder, shattering my elbow and wrist. It was bad enough that the surgeon who helped put all the little bits of bone back in the right place told me that not so long ago I might well have had it amputated. Dancing with the ensuing vulnerability in the months that followed required me to develop a much more attentive and tender way of listening to my body, which I'm incredibly grateful for. There were many times when I needed some emotional release but couldn't do my usual cathartic and carefree flinging myself around, so I had to learn how to let go within the limitation of caring for my arm. Exploring 'How the hell do I manage that?' was the beginning of what I would describe as the second half of my life in movement practice – way more subtle, humbled and surrendered. If I had believed the thought 'I can't dance properly with a broken arm', I would have deprived myself of these teachings, missing the gold in favour of waiting for normal to return.

Difficulties are a good sign. They give you something to wrestle with, which will greatly accelerate your learning and strengthen your relationship with the divine mystery that is coming through you when you dance. Good days are fine, but usually not as transformative or revelatory as those days when you don't feel like it. That's when to seize the day and – with all the heartfelt calling that you found through your work in Chapter 4 (*Discipline, Devotion and Desperation*) – make time to move. I doubt you'll regret it.

On the other hand, if you believe the thought that says 'I don't feel like it, so I'd be better off doing something else' and go through your day without having spent a moment with your practice, that slump-shape may well hang around all day like a bad fog.

Most obstacles to practice are actually opportunities to expand and deepen, appearing as discomfort. They are worthy of your attention. Rather than trying to get rid of anything, how about making space for what's there, with curiosity and compassion?

Let's take these problematic thought-forms one by one. They can all be serious concerns at times, so let's look at how best to approach each obstacle in a way that can make movement practice an enjoyable part of your day, affecting your life truly enough that you notice the difference, gladly.

Problems as Portals:

Thought #1: 'I don't have enough space/time'

Space: you might want a great big open dance studio that you can cartwheel across without bumping into anything, but you don't *need* it. Work with what you've got. Push the sofa back a bit, maybe move the fish tank, but give it a go as it is. We always have to work within limitations, and this is one of them.

If the limitations of your space wind you up, how about getting interested in that?

Practise: Space (≥5m)

Get yourself moving to warm up and ground yourself in your physical presence. Be practical, encouraging your whole body to be involved.

Once your blood is pumping a little warmer, pause for a moment and sense into the experience of having limited space. What is it triggering in you? Is it frustration or fear? A kind of collapse? Could you be curious about that rather than wishing it away?

How does it show up in your body? Can you breathe into it, begin to let it shape you, move you? How might that feeling-state express itself in movement and sound?

Find the vast freedom that comes through surrendering to the state of being limited, opening to the space inside you.

Time: During an initial coaching session to look at home practice, I often address this issue. Often, people believe that they have to dance for at least 20 minutes for it to be worthwhile, preferably an hour.

At least at first, I'd say even 20 minutes is too much. Scale it back. How about 7 minutes? Or 3? Even one minute can radically change your state. Seriously, kick that protestant work ethic out the window and listen for what you *love* instead. Mix together what you long for with what's do-able for you today, and enjoy the result.

Far better to have a loving commitment with yourself to practice for 5 minutes a day in the morning and achieve it for a whole week than to set yourself a goal of dancing for 45 minutes no matter what and failing on day 2.

Practise: Time (≥1m)

Ask yourself, what amount of time would be a pleasure to move for today? What would you relish with an inner 'Yes please!'

Now dance for less time than that. For example, if you would look forward to moving for 5 minutes, limit yourself to 3.

Notice how it feels, and how your relationship with your practice is affected.

Thought #2: 'I don't have the right music'

Of course, we humans love to dance to a beat. Put music on and watch a toddler who's learning to walk: they'll stand there, bouncing their little knees in time with the beat with a big smile on their face. But there's more to movement than dancing, and there are ways of dancing beyond the beat that are well worth learning.

As I mentioned earlier, practising without music has many benefits:

- You can usually follow your own energy much more fluidly and sensitively when there's no music in the way. This is particularly true if you've got strong feelings going on. It's like the difference between walking on a path that others who came before you have created and striking out into uncharted wilderness. There's nothing wrong with established pathways, but that wilderness is you. Take an interest and get into it.

- Practising without music will make you stronger, and you'll have the capacity to enjoy music even more when it's there. If you 'need' music to practise, that's a dependency, which will make you weak. You can find strength in connection to your breath and body, your own inspiration, your own guidance. Develop good practice on that foundation; then, when there is music, it can be such a pleasure.
- Silence is quicker and easier! There is nothing to prepare, unless you want to light a candle and turn off the phone. This is especially good if you only have a short time to practice. Just move with the sound of your breath and your footsteps.

Practise: Moving without music (≥5m)

Use a timer, so you have a frame within which to explore.

Let the silence and the space draw your attention inwards, appreciating the sensitivity and subtlety that comes with it. Begin to move into that silence, paying attention to the physical quality of your body in the physical space you have.

Listen inside. How are you feeling emotionally? How might you use your movement to express those feelings?

If there's a not-knowing quality without the guidance of music, how might you embody that?

Notice your breath, allowing it to move in and out freely with the swirl of your body.

Once you're done, take a moment to be still, savouring the silence even more deeply.

Rest. Ahhhh....

Thought #3: 'I don't have the discipline'

Question: what's driving you? Is it a judgemental imperative to improve yourself, or is it a longing, a yearning, for something you know but can't quite define? Is your sense of discipline based on love or war?

It's amazing how easy it is to get into wars with ourselves. Speaking personally, I am intimately aware of the tendency to believe there's something wrong with me, there's somewhere I need to get to that I am not, and I frequently go to work on myself with a deep-set harshness that is, frankly, cruel.

Now, there's nothing wrong with wanting to be somewhere you're not. That's a natural desire, part of being alive. Even the lilies of the valley are reaching up, aren't they? But do you reach up for the love of sunlight and love of your own flourishing, or are you impelled by a subtle shame or dislike of your ground, of your present state? Have you imbibed mainstream culture to the point where you're a living embodiment of it, driven by a mindless imperative towards growth at all costs, believing that you are worthless unless you're working, including working on yourself?

Is there a part of you insisting that you should be practising like a Tibetan monk, otherwise it's all a useless waste of time?

That task-master attitude to practice is a killer. If this is strong for you, how about inviting the task-master to dance?

Practise: dancing the disciplinarian (≥10m)

Get yourself moving to warm up and ground yourself in your physical presence. Be practical, encouraging your whole body to be involved.

Once your blood is pumping a little warmer, become still and sense into yourself for that task-master. Where do you feel it in your body? What's its emotional tone like? What's its voice like?

Now that you have a sense of them, let their character sculpt your body into a stance or posture. Take on their shape. Use your whole body for this, not only your arms and hands. How do they stand? Are their hips thrust forwards or tipped sideways?

Once you're embodying them from head to toe, you can begin to explore how they move, how they breathe, what they say. Go for it! What does this part of you want? What does it care about? What is its purpose? Let this disciplinarian have their space without holding back, allowing the movements to go beyond your habitual styles. Be willing to enjoy it! Go on a journey, following through all the twists and turns of it until you feel complete. It might pause sometimes, then take off again. It might change radically as you go, for example starting off angry and ending up needy. Trust the process, and trust your body to take you through it.

In this way, you're stepping into 'their' energy so that you can claim it back for yourself, this 'part' of you becoming integral now, onside rather than against you.

Then it might be useful to write for a while: How else might you use this energy in your life if you weren't beating yourself up with it? How might that change you? What would be a good creative outlet for you if this quality remained well integrated rather than a marginalised problem?

Thought #4: 'My experience should be similar to what I've become used to in a class'

This expectation may bring up either a fear of failure or of being overwhelmed. If you can't recreate the intensity you've found in a class with a big group, a teacher, and loud music, you might think you're not doing it properly. On the other hand, you may fear that if you did recreate that intensity, you could be completely out of your depth, unable to handle it on your own.

The truth is, it's not going to be like it is in a class. It can't be — that context is powerful, and moving on your own is utterly different. Drop your expectations, open your mind, and find out who you are when you are the author of your own experience.

Be willing to learn slowly, bit by bit. It's a craft, a landscape, a pathway. Notice what goes well and appreciate yourself for it.

Practise: moving with expectations and letting them go (≥7m)

Get yourself moving to warm up and ground yourself in your physical presence. Be practical, encouraging your whole body to be involved.

Once your blood is pumping a little warmer, pause for a moment, and focus on your expectation, and allow it to take shape through your whole body. What position for your feet? How are your hands, your hips, your back? Where do your eyes go? Breathe life into it with a repetition — does it rock back and forth a bit, rise and fall, expand and contract? Let the movement grow until it's fully expressive, wholehearted.

Then let it go, walking around your space, shedding it step by step with deep clear breaths, shaking it off.

Now... begin to move in the empty space and find out who you are when it's truly up to you.

Thought #5: 'I would miss the group energy' or 'I miss the contact with other people'

I understand. We're wired for connection, and the experience of dancing with others is one of the most enjoyable, enlivening, expansive ways we can be with each other. The energy of a whole group in motion is quite a hit, and together we can usually go a lot further than we could alone.

At the time of writing, we're at the tail end of a long, long series of lockdowns, which has brought into sharp relief the loneliness that was already endemic throughout the post-indigenous world. By all means, keep going to classes, spaces where you can practise in company. Even at home, you could invite friends, lovers, or children to dance with you, if they are willing.

But you'll get to know yourself in valuable new ways if you go through this fear of missing others, and there's a freedom and independence to be found in your own company. You probably won't get anything like the same high you would in a group session, but highs are not the only things worth living for.

Acquaint yourself with the valleys, and any quiet fears you have of them.

Learn to love your own company, and any grief that's biding its time there.

Practise: being alone (≥7m)

Enter into your practice with no agenda other than to be honest with yourself. Drop into movement and allow the natural flow of what comes. If it's quiet, gentle, or weary even, can you surrender to that? Be with it? Be curious about that experience? Who among us in this modern age doesn't need a little more restfulness? Rather than missing the wild high of a group, could you appreciate the lush valley of solitude?

If you are lonely, can you let yourself feel what that's like? Can you let it move you, drawing your breath deep into where it hurts and allowing your body to be shaped by it? Can you let it cut into you until you're breaking open? Can you stay with yourself right through until you find your love for the fragile mote of humanity that you are, glad of your own company, grateful to be alive, sweetened by the salt of your tears?

Thought #6: 'I don't believe it would be useful' or 'I couldn't do it properly'

Most of us are plagued by self-doubts deep down. Rather than talking yourself out of them, how about getting curious about these thoughts, and the feelings that go along with them?

Practise: I can't... (≥10m)

Get yourself moving to warm up and ground yourself in your physical presence. Be practical, encouraging your whole body to be involved.

Once your blood is pumping a little warmer, pause a moment, and sense into that quality of self-doubt. Where do you feel it in your body? Is there an emotional energy around that, such as anxiety, frustration, or hopelessness?

What physical shape goes with that feeling state, and the sensations in your body? Use your whole body to align yourself with it, giving yourself to it rather than fighting it. Breathe deeply into it.

Begin to allow that shape to move, finding its dance, allowing it to twist your way out of 'normal' postures and allowing any feelings that are coming up to find full expression through your body and breath.

What are the thoughts that go along with this? Keeping it as pithy as you can — for example simply 'I can't do it!' — speak or even shout them out loud while you move, allowing the words to intensify the feelings, adding them to the movements already happening.

Keep exploring until you're done, give yourself time to settle, and then appreciate yourself, literally saying out loud 'I appreciate myself for being willing to face this painful stuff'. Maybe put your arms around yourself as you do so, giving yourself a hug.

Thought #7: 'I'm scared of what might happen, especially of strong feelings coming up and being alone with that'

In all my conversations with students and clients about home practice, this is one of the most common fears that crops up. In a group context, with loud music and someone facilitating the journey, it's not unusual to have profound, even life-changing experiences, with stronger emotional forces moving through us than we've ever dared to face. It's easy to imagine that kind of intensity being too much at home alone.

It's likely that this fear is unfounded. Moving solo, with quieter music or none at all, for a shorter time, there's much less to stir you up. The chances are that your practice will stay well within the bounds of what you can handle. Your psyche is astonishingly well-honed at gauging its own limits.

There are no guarantees though, and it may be that you do get overwhelmed. Movement practice, like the rest of life, is not entirely safe. If like me you love a good adventure, this makes it all the more compelling! If on the other hand you find yourself staying away from practice in order to avoid that fear, then how about Focusing on the fear itself?

Becoming intimate with your fear is a profound journey, with the potential for big implications in your daily life over time. Leaning into our fears builds courage, and gives us more freedom.

Practise: on the edge (≥7m)

Get yourself moving to warm up and ground yourself in your physical presence. Be practical, encouraging your whole body to be involved.

Once your blood is pumping a little warmer, pause for a moment, and sense your fear of deep experience and breathe into it, noticing how and where you feel it in your body. Allow the fear to be there, even thanking it for protecting you. Inwardly lean into it a little, letting yourself feel the quality of this fear.

Rebalance by walking briskly, even courageously, around the room. Take big strides, looking around you, swinging your arms, taking strong lungfuls of air and exhaling through your mouth as well as your nose.

Repeat this as many times as you wish, leaning into the fear, then coming back out again, practising moving towards and away from it.

Now get some paper and give the pen to your fear. Let it write, or draw, and tell you about itself.

Practise: into the depths (≥10m)

Get yourself moving to warm up and ground yourself in your physical presence. Be practical, encouraging your whole body to be involved.

Once your blood is pumping a little warmer, pause for a moment, and begin to sense into the fear of your depths, breathing into it, noticing where you feel it in your body.

Allow the fears to shape you, move through you, engaging your whole body, especially your feet, legs, hips. Let it be dynamic — adrenaline needs to move! Relaxing your jaw, breathe openly through your mouth. Let sounds out too, if that feels useful. Your body is designed to handle fear brilliantly; let the wisdom of millions of years of evolution take over and release all that energy through shaking, trembling, thrashing around in whatever way feels right.

As you move, notice that this feeling-state you're in has power. It's yours. It's your life energy, part of the creative force that is your essential nature. Enjoy it. Make the most of it, letting it grow you, expand you, empower you to choose your path, walk your talk and be a light in the world, ennobled by your vulnerability.

Now get some paper and give the pen to that energy. Let it write, or draw, have a voice.

Thought #8: 'I don't value myself enough to do it'

In the many, many times in my life when I've hated myself, seen myself as worthless or downright toxic, I've often added a whole other layer to that, judging myself for judging myself. If that's true for you, could you find some acceptance for the way it is right now? Have some compassion for that? The way we value or devalue ourselves has its roots in our infancy and young childhood, way before we had any choice in the matter, which can make it a stubbornly persistent pattern. Even a tiny bit of kindness can go a long way – could you accept that this is how it is right now?

As parents we do the best we can, but we're often driven by forces beyond our control. If we're determined or well-resourced or blessed, we might become more conscious of those drivers in the process, but probably only partially so. We pass on what we have not integrated to our children, so if you don't value yourself much, turn and acknowledge your parents for your wounding, and then stand within that maelstrom, knowing it's your responsibility now, and begin to make medicine.

The way to do that is to feel the pain and turn it into art: become a moving, breathing, living work of art. Dance your stuff until you come through the other side.

Practise: into the heart of low self-worth (≥15m) 

Get yourself moving to warm up and ground yourself in your physical presence. Be practical, encouraging your whole body to be involved.

Once your blood is pumping a little warmer, pause for a moment. Maybe close your eyes. Maybe place one hand on your heart, another on your belly. Ask yourself, 'Where is this lack of self-worth, and how does it feel in my body?'

Be with the question, listening inside with an openness to whatever arises. Maybe you feel strong emotions coming up, or maybe memories, voices, impressions. It's probably a young part of you, so could you welcome it and thank it for showing itself, with the kindness you might offer a child?

Once you have a sense of this insecure place in you, open your eyes again and begin to explore how to move with it. Find the shapes, the breath, the footsteps. Don't try to save yourself — surrender to whatever comes, letting it twist you into strange or wild patterns of motion. Maybe it's not wild at all though — it could be a kind of deadness that comes — but that too is a dance, dropping into slumps, flops and lifeless poses.

Feel how you feel about being this way, adding that to the mix of what is being embodied, expressed, released. As you go, keep using your skill as a dancer to let your body handle whatever comes up, using movement, breath, sounds.

When you're done, grab pen and paper, and write. Write from the heart, expressing all that you feel, see, and long for. Or write a letter to your parents saying all you never said. Or write a lament to your God, asking for help.

Let the words spill out of you, and then make a conscious choice about what to do with the result: burn it, bury it, make a collage with it, send it?

Thought #9: 'My neighbours would be disturbed' or 'I don't have any privacy' or 'the kids are always around'

In our home, we have to be careful about when we play music loudly, which is hard for me. I'd love to bang it out late at night sometimes, or at six in the morning. It's not just music though; I love to use my voice when I'm moving too. We've told our neighbours about our practice, explaining its purpose and how valuable it is for us. At least I know they're not going to call the police if they hear me shouting like a madman.

One way out of the neighbours problem is to move outdoors. But if you need to stay indoors, isn't something better than nothing? It is for me. If I've got kids asleep early in the morning, I'd rather take time to move quietly with no music (or with Bluetooth earbuds) than nothing. Also, most days, I'd rather get up early enough to do that than wait until later in the day or miss out altogether.

You could explore the experience of being limited, as in *Practise: moving within limitations* limitations (see next page) but there are other ways to turn this obstacle into practice. The limitation of having to be quiet has sometimes brought me to a different kind of intensity in my movement. It has nudged me to use my breath more, to concentrate harder, pouring energy through a clearer channel than what might have otherwise just been a relatively careless crash-bang-wallop dance.

When my kids were little, I loved doing my practice with them. It changed the way I moved and limited what I could dive into, but that was better than nothing and there was the bonus delight of being with them in a different way. Once they got older, I'd ask them to give me some alone time.

Micro-practices can be great to enjoy with children – mine love it when I bust out of normal, upright adult-mode for a moment in the kitchen.

Micro-Practise: with children

You're with the kids: stay awake to your feeling nature, your emotional currents. When something comes up, express it physically instead of verbally. Or both. Let them see how you feel in your facial expression as well as your posture. Exaggerate everything and make it fun, even funny. Find a way to be yourself that won't blow their fuses or frighten them, allowing your feelings to show through your body as we all do naturally when very young, whilst staying in relationship with them.

This can be a strong thing to do as a parent. Raising children is one of the most deeply demanding creative endeavours there is, and like anything you approach creatively, there are no hard and fast rules that always work. Best to practise this way of being with them at first when you're not emotionally charged. Let them get used to you being physical before you let loose a high voltage catharsis that is totally left-field for them!

Some years ago I had a very tempestuous period with one of my sons, with a lot of anger between us. He still teases me about the way I moved at times when I got mad at him. There were many times when my parenting of him was far from ideal, but at least he saw me deal with my feelings to some extent physically, not attempting to channel everything through my head.

Practise: moving within limitations (≥10m)  

What would be OK for the neighbours? Maybe it's just loud music that would be a problem, or maybe you have to be careful with your feet for people living downstairs. Have the intention to practice within those limitations, and then get yourself moving to warm up and ground yourself in your physical presence. Be practical, encouraging your whole body to be involved.

Once your blood is pumping a little warmer, pause for a moment and sense into the experience of being constricted by limitations. What is it triggering in you? Is it frustration or fear? A kind of collapse? Could you be curious about that rather than wishing it away?

How does it show up in your body? Can you breathe into it, begin to let it shape you, move you? How might that feeling-state express itself in movement and sound, whilst still staying within the limitations you have?

Find the freedom that comes through surrendering to what is. Be a dedicated artist, determined to paint even though you only have a small canvas.

Thought #10: 'I'm too distracted by daily life'

The choice of where to place your attention is perhaps your most fundamental power.

There are times when we need to take ourselves in hand like a warm-hearted but firm father and say, 'No, we're not doing that right now; we're doing this.'

You probably know yourself well enough to figure it out: what amount of time can you spare? What time of day would work best for you? Then it's a clear choice. Excuses can be gently dealt with or ignored.

What will you choose?

Practise: giving attention (≥7m)

i) First, do the dance of being completely, hopelessly distracted. Flail around with your arms and hands, reaching for impossible goals everywhere, footsteps staggering around the space aimlessly, breath ragged and rough. Move like you're being buffeted by invisible winds blowing in all directions. Do it wholeheartedly enough for it to be fun.

ii) Now abruptly stop. Be still, noticing your breath, tuning in to your physicality. Make space for any feelings that come up. Listen inside for a part of your body that calls for your attention — it could be a tiny point somewhere, or it could be something like your whole left side. It could be where you feel the most energy, or it could be a quiet, gentle place.

iii) Focus your attention into that part of you and explore how it moves, breathing into it, allowing it full expression. Wholeheartedly give the rest of your body to follow its lead. Open your mind and engage your creativity to explore how it shapes you, valuing small movements, strange shapes, subtle impressions. Be curious about how things unfold if you simply give attention, allowing this part of you to lead without any agenda for it to change, giving it space to show you new ways to move.

iv) Be still again and appreciate yourself for the exploration.

Thought #11: 'I'm too self-conscious — it would feel weird'

Self-consciousness can be a euphemism for shame, which might be deep rooted and very strong, in which case you may need to approach it very tenderly, over many sessions, even getting some support from someone else if you find yourself out of your depth, or chronically stuck.

It could also be more of a mental habit though, where you pick at yourself with concerns like 'Do I look OK?' or 'Am I doing it right?' or 'Am I normal enough to be acceptable to you, world?' That might require some bold moves, breaking free from our small-mindedness with a big loud dance, full of fire and gusto.

Chances are, you grew up with parents who were less than enlightened, in which case you would have had to constrict yourself, being less than fully yourself in order to stay psychologically close to them.

Self-consciousness is the monitoring of the protective mechanism you developed to keep you safely within 'acceptably normal'. You probably went on from that parental imprint to include your teachers, your peers as a teenager, and society at large.

Whether to let any of this stop you or not is another choice. No need for it to be a harsh one, but it could be a firm one, made with deep compassion for yourself and the human condition. You could take yourself lovingly in hand, and decide to explore what's there for you, what comes up if you move with nobody watching.

Practise: being real (≥10m)

i) Stand in the middle of your space. Keeping your feet firmly in one spot, look around you, literally scanning around the whole room with your eyes, turning your head and rotating your spine as far as you can, first one way, then the other. This helps let your nervous system know that you're safe from any outside attack.

ii) Now turn your attention inside. Can you sense your self-consciousness? Where do you feel it in your body? What is its feeling tone? What are the sensations?

iii) Breathe into that sense of self-consciousness and let it de-form you, twisting your whole body into a shape in alignment with the feeling, maybe one that you wouldn't normally think of as 'me'. Embrace any tension, awkwardness, or discomfort. Feel it.

iv) Now allow the feeling to express itself even more vibrantly through a repetition-movement, going from this shape to another and back again, over and over, in rhythm with your breath. Let the exhale come out of your mouth, allowing sound to come if it wants to.

v) Surrender yourself completely to the feeling, allowing your body to do whatever it wants to do. Dance that self-consciousness right through the bones, the blood, the breath of you. Let it bring you more alive, more passionate, more conscious. Let this dance run its course, all the way through to a still point, then relax into that pause, opening into the spaciousness you've created within yourself.

vi) Find a way to appreciate yourself for your practice, maybe saying out loud, 'I appreciate myself for doing this', or wrapping your arms around yourself like a big hug.

vii) Bonus: write a wild poem about being a free spirit!

Thought #12: 'I need structure, and don't know how to create it'

I've approached each of the above obstacles to practice as a 'stone in your shoe' that can become a gateway in itself – something to be curious about.

This one's a little different. Whilst you could enter into a practice session and explore what it feels like to move without a structure, even that intention itself creates a kind of structure. It's actually impossible to do anything without some kind of structure, so the question is more about creating structures intentionally that are useful for you.

Hopefully this book will have given you lots of great ideas about how to do that, but let's recap what we know.

The most straightforward structure to use is time: set a timer.

Another way to create structure is with music. These days there are lots of movement teachers offering playlists on Spotify, Soundcloud or Mixcloud.

You could use a practice you've learnt with a teacher, adapting it to suit your needs.

You could also find a structure in any of the examples in this chapter. Look back over these obstacles to practice and try out a specific exercise to work with.

However, as I said, just having a clear intention creates a structure. When I stepped out from the 5Rhythms world to create ZeroOne, I set myself the task of exploring movement without any structure for a while, because I noticed that I was so steeped in the 5Rhythms perception that my mind was constantly assessing my movement through that lens. It took over a year of that consistent intent to shake off the habit, but I loved the investigation and was astonished at how trapped I'd been without knowing it. That intention to work without structure paradoxically created a structure in itself.

What's your intention today, for your practice? Could you lean into that as your structure, with nothing else to hold onto?

Practise: moving with intention (≥3m)

Listen inside yourself to get a sense of what your intention is for today's practice. You don't have to make it up in your head; it's already there in your body. Feel for it.

Putting things into words is powerful, especially if you can get to the essence of it without waffling. As simply as you can, either speak your intention out loud or write it down.

Then drop into movement with that intention as your only guide.

Bon voyage...

Obstacles to Practice Endnotes

I feel terrible this morning. Dragging myself into practice with a heavy body, I'm emotionally numb, mentally foggy. I can't settle on anything, casting about from one thing to another, attempting to embody the heaviness, then trying to throw it off with big breaths and vigorous movement, then collapsing with a kind of hopeless resignation.

After a while, I finish, totally unsatisfied, frustrated, judging myself for wasting my time with shoddy practice. If anything, I feel worse than when I started.

The whole day goes badly.

Sometimes practice just is crummy. There are days when my efforts seem useless, and I may as well have eaten some toast or read the news. Well, maybe not quite, but almost.

Practice is occasionally like that, but not often. Movement is powerful, and usually the days when I don't feel like it are the most productive of all. Countless times I've started as in the story above, dragging myself onto the floor, and found within a few minutes that I'm actually angry about something, or needing to shed some tears, and the movement helps everything to loosen up and rearrange itself within me. I've learnt over time to be extra curious about myself when I don't feel like practising, and to be quite firm with myself about trying it.

14: Letting It Go

Let go or be dragged — Zen proverb

This morning, I wake with a longing to be ordinary. The day goes by in that way. I make some tea, sit on the sofa doing nothing, spend a few hours outside digging, hang out with a friend, drink a beer, watch a movie. That's another way to be in meditation, another way to dance.

You can learn a lot by focusing on specifics such as these obstacles to practice. You can also grow deeply by dedicating yourself to movement practice, especially if you embrace all the modes described in this book. You can heal many wounds, accept many limitations and go beyond others. You can become a skilled practitioner, gathering medicine along the way that could help others, becoming faithful to the light you're born to be.

However...

Sometimes all that 'work' gets a bit worthy.

There are times when it's best to just let go.

Some days, the best practice is no practice at all. If you're anything like me, it's all too easy to see yourself as a problem, with practice as a solution. It's only in the last few years that I've been at peace enough to not obsess over improving myself as though I'm fighting a fire, but to simply enjoy where I am.

How about you? Are you endlessly chipping away at yourself, trying to make yourself a better person? Could you take a break and enjoy – or at least accept – being as you are, no more, no less?

Maybe just do nothing today. Or put on some great music, invite a friend or get the kids involved, throw open the windows and dance for fun, for joy, for pleasure.

Fuck trying to be conscious, or to improve yourself. Don't forget to party.

Drop It

There's another way to let go of all that serious dedication to 'good practice', which has become more my style as I've got older. Rather than partying, I just drop it.

I've worked so damn hard on myself for so long, and I've achieved what I set out to do: that is, come to terms with my wounding in a way that has brought me to some kind of peace with myself. My nervous system is still often in high-alert mode, and I easily fall into shame. When I'm in a confident mood, that can spill over into arrogance, making me callous and careless in the way I relate to others. However, I'm quicker to regain my centre when I go off-balance, and I'm not nearly so hard on myself when I mess up.

A new way of practising movement has emerged for me in the last few years; a kind of 'Nothing to Achieve' practice. I love it so much it almost hurts. There's a sense of 'The Emergency is Over', but along with the relief of that, there's an echo of the pain of the gruelling years. It's something like an awash-with-gratitude grieving.

It's early morning. I'm in London staying with my brother, and in a couple of hours I'll take the Eurostar to Brussels where I'm working over the weekend. The workshop will very likely be intense. It's one of my favourites: 'Fierce Loving'. People will probably go through a lot.

I, on the other hand, don't feel like going through anything. With an immense rush of gratitude, I realise that I don't have to right now. I'm already here.

I dance slowly on a small prayer rug, going nowhere. I have no goal at all. Just being. I don't move vigorously, and I don't breathe particularly deeply. There's nothing to fix, and no hell to escape from. I am at peace with myself, despite being deeply flawed.

I weep with gratitude at being alive and being as I am, and it's a kind of grieving-as-loving, a blessing that hurts right where I've always hurt, but in a grateful way.

I love being in meditation, and I love to be physical — not to achieve anything, but just for the love of it. I'm OK with myself as I am.

No more working on anything, for now.

I still love to dance, not to get anywhere, and not exactly for fun, but more because I just like being me, and 'me' is a dance.

Ending Endnotes

I'm nine years old, in school assembly, singing the hymn 'To Be a Pilgrim'. I am suddenly overwhelmed with emotion as I realise that more than anything in the world I long to be a pilgrim myself. Somehow, I manage to keep singing despite the choking grief of love in my throat and the tears rolling, uncool, down my cheeks.

I have no context within which to understand this moment. No one I know becomes a pilgrim. This is the 1970s, in England.

I almost completely forgot about this until my early fifties, when it came back to me and I realised in a flash that my dream has come true. I have devoted my life to some kind of spiritual path, albeit distracted, faltering, wayward by any standards. But deep down, that's what I've done. That's where my devotion has gone.

Those tears I shed as a boy roll down my cheeks all over again as I write, this time with astonishment and gratitude at the quiet grace that life is capable of bestowing on us and guiding us with, unawares.

The way I've described practice modes in this book is how it's been for me, and I hope it's useful for you. I hope it deepens your fascination with your Pathway Home, and opens your eyes to a broader horizon.

Maybe you'll travel far enough to see many limitations in these pages, going far beyond them and truly forging your own way.

As time goes by, you may notice that Open, Focus, Surrender and Give all merge into one at times, along with Zero. That is the deeper reality, clichéd yet true: All really is One.

In the end, that One is us, and we are the dance, and the dance is life, and life is divine, and the divine is... Zero.

In the end, all distinctions and forms disappear as we become the alchemical mix of Zero and One: a dance.

So let us take another step, grateful to have a breath still upon us.

My movement practice has been my pilgrimage, and the many thousands of you who have studied with me over almost thirty years have been an integral part of that. Despite a deep-down loneliness that has dogged me most of my life until very recently, I have been able to sense you walking alongside me, and you've made a difference. You have inspired me, encouraged me, helped me notice that what I'm doing is worth something. In seeing your growth, healing and joy in life, I have been able to notice my own, which has kept me going.

It's only in the last few years that I've begun to experience myself as truly in connection with others, with nothing in the way. Until that began to happen, I didn't know it was missing. I didn't know I could feel this way. 'Family' is no longer agonising. My parents now live up the road, and sharing life with them is a pleasure. My brother is my most steadfast friend. I love being a father, and a grandfather now, too. Perhaps all that solo practice helped me to reach through my deepest wounds and allow myself to be touched. Perhaps my pathway led me to discover, rather late in life, that 'home' is not only inside, but with others. Perhaps that's why I've finally felt able to write this book.

A few key friends, family members, healers and teachers have seen me through this homecoming, but most of all, I am more grateful than I can say to Maria-Carin. Your gentleness, kindness, humour, and ruthless insistence upon honesty astonishes and delights me daily, and I would not have written this book in the way I have without you. You got to me, and you've got me, and I couldn't be more glad.

If you, dear reader, were one of those fellow travellers in years gone by, thank you. Really, thank you. If you've just come alongside for the short time it takes to read these pages, thank you too. Welcome to the path that creates itself as you walk. May it take you where we're all going. I'm sure it will. There's nowhere else, and we're already here.

One last practice for if you've danced through these pages, trying out many of the possibilities contained here, enough to have a sense of having travelled some way, and not being quite where you were when you started:

Practise: taking another step

Put the book down, stand yourself up and take a breath.

Look around and know that something has changed as a result of your travails.

Take one more step, along with a breath, and be glad, knowing that you've barely begun, yet you have begun, and that life is still ahead of you with all of its unknowns. Knowing that tomorrow, your practice will be waiting for you, and yours it is.

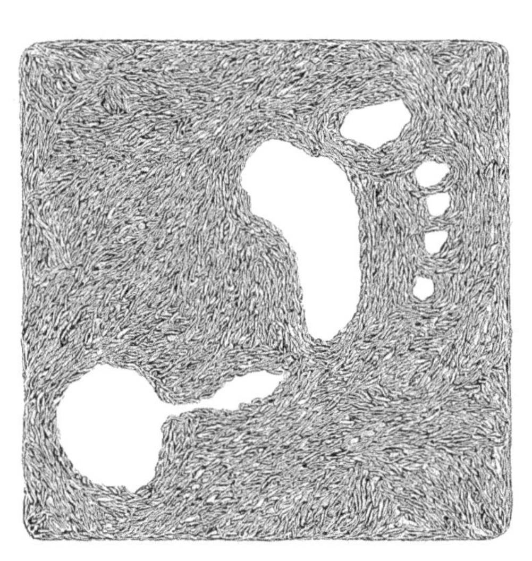

And in the end
The love you take
Is equal to the love you make
— The Beatles

Appendix I: Movement Modalities

My lineage comes from Gabrielle Roth and her brilliant insights into the nature of human reality that became the 5Rhythms. Listed here are modalities that have grown from that root, all of which I can recommend. I know all of the founders personally, and can vouch for their dedication, integrity, and bold creativity.

Most of them have a range of facilitators offering the practices who will themselves have a range of experience under their belt. Explore, and seek out the teachers you can trust and learn from.

Their work is listed in the order that it emerged:

5Rhythms	5rhythms.com
Soul Motion	soulmotionnextsteps.com
Moves Into Consciousness	movesintoconsciousness.com
Movement Medicine	movementmedicine.com
Open Floor	openfloor.org
Azul	pathofazul.com
The 360 Emergence	the360emergence.com
ZeroOne	inzero.one

Also worth mentioning is the phenomenon of Ecstatic Dance, less formal or organised than the above practices, and which evolved from people who liked the form of the 5Rhythms but didn't want to be officially part of that world. I have been to a few of these over the years and didn't really like any of them, finding them to be missing a sense of focus or grounded discipline. However, recently, I was lucky enough to dance at a session with an Ecstatic Dance DJ who blew all of my prejudices clean out of the water with his tender mastery.

Then there are other movement practices which have different roots entirely. Many of these I'm sure have a great deal to offer but I do not have the experience needed to vouch for them. Explore with discernment; as in all fields of human endeavour, there will be a wide range of quality and depth wherever you look, with some ungrounded nonsense to be found amongst the good stuff.

Appendix II: Trauma

The recent upsurge of awareness and interest in the phenomenon we call trauma has revealed such widespread prevalence that we could almost call it a universal part of the human experience. Trauma is not something that happens to you; it's an internal response to events. Our nervous system begins to exhibit traumatised patterns when we get too much of something, too fast or too soon, or are deprived of something we truly need for too long, with too little healthy connection from emotionally balanced people we trust. The core of these patterns is a disconnection from our inner sense of self, undertaken when we couldn't cope with our inner experience in any other way. We can develop this state through a single overwhelming event or in response to relatively minor violations, deprivations or stresses that repeat for some time, whether we're aware of them or not.

If we suffer in these ways as children (and almost everyone does to some extent at some point) the effect is complicated by our dependency on adults. The distorted responses in our developing nervous system, vital for our emotional survival at the time, can remain long after they're useful, forming what we now call developmental trauma. It seems to me that the way of life most of the world is now pursuing is a direct outcome of millennia of unresolved trauma that emerged particularly within Europe and was violently exported around the world. As a result, the distortions we call developmental trauma are a spectrum that almost everyone is on, rendering us to some extent dysfunctional in the way we manage ourselves, our relationships, and our work.

These patterns also include habits, compulsions, cravings or addictive behaviours that seem to soothe or distract us from the pain underneath them whilst making it worse in the long term.

Most people pass the bulk of these wounds on to their children and the world at large, more or less haplessly, either intact or in their mirror image. (By mirror image I mean that, being determined to 'never be like my father', we overcompensate and create a kind of reversed shape impact.) A huge value of doing inner work is to become conscious of these wounds, neutralising at least some of the distortions like a lightning conductor so they are not passed on. Instead, we pass on the incredibly hopeful and bright legacy of being able to go through difficulties and thrive.

Movement work has the potential to bring up what is unconscious in you, including your pain and fear and including any childhood or other trauma. That's one of its gifts, and if you've got a solid grounding of trust in your own being, some good friends and family to talk to about what you're going through, and the courage to keep going when things get difficult, you could heal and grow a great deal.

If you are suffering from severe trauma however, chances are that you might not have that grounding, or trust, or support. At least, not as much as you need. If you're doubtful about your ability to handle what may come up, get some professional support to work with it rather than attempting to deal with it alone.

There's much you can do on your own, but a key component of trauma patterns is emotional isolation, and there will be some stages of the journey you cannot do alone. This is particularly important if you're dealing with trauma that's rooted in childhood. Find a trained professional you can trust. Below you'll find a list of possible resources for that.

When you have the right support, solo movement practice can be a potent ingredient in your healing process, which in the end is not about getting rid of wounds so much as reintegrating the parts of us that were necessarily avoided, suppressed, or outlawed. The word 'heal' comes from the same root as the word 'whole', and all the practices in this book will tend to pull you in that direction: towards your own wholeness.

Beyond that, the process of integrating traumatic experiences and reconnecting with what has been exiled often becomes a kind of life-breakthrough, with wounds giving rise to specific gifts that couldn't be found any other way. We make medicine for our wounds in the healing of them, and then we have that medicine to pass on to others. As Bhagavan Dass says, 'The wound is the key'. Our most precious light comes from our most painful darkness.

If you're suffering in these ways, I wish you the courage to find your way. I wish you well. It's been a long and often torturous path for me to deal with the wounding I endured as a young child, and I can tell you: I have found better days, and learning to dance, move, breathe, and cry out for help has all been absolutely invaluable. Reach out to someone, somehow, and take some steps.

Trauma Modalities

Each person's path through their healing is unique and you may find that different things help at different times; like you, your healing will evolve. Many modalities have their origins in psychology or bodywork, both of which are vital for the biopsychosocial healing you are undertaking.

Current research shows that two key aspects that support transformation are titration (small, incrementally tolerated experiences) and a 'bottom up' approach (using physiological input and awareness from the body first, then the cognition). Added to that, it is vital to find a practitioner whom you feel basically alright to be with, and who can create a safe container in which to move through to greater wholeness.

The list below is long because I' m attempting to be thorough at the time of writing. If it seems overwhelming to look through, and you need some pointers which way to go, I'd suggest that if you have anyone in your life you trust enough to ask for advice then do so. You could also scan down the list, let a handful of options stand out and then do some research online about each one, paying close attention to how you feel when you're reading about each one. If any of them seem to 'click', then follow them up further.

When actually choosing a practitioner, again play close attention to the feelings in your body while in communication with them, and if at any point you get a strong sense of 'Not OK', then back off, with no explanation necessary other than 'It just doesn't feel quite right in my body, and I'm choosing to trust that.'

Brain Spotting

Compassionate Inquiry

Eye Movement Desensitization and Reprocessing (EMDR)

Integral Somatic Psychology

Internal Body Psychotherapy

Internal Family Systems

NeuroAffective Relational Model

Sensory Motor Psychotherapy

Somatic Experiencing

Somatic Practice

Somatic Psychology

Transforming the Experienced Brain

The NICAMB website may be a good place to start, which includes free resources you can explore.

Other modalities that can be supportive if undertaken with trauma-informed practitioners:

Acupuncture

Bowen Therapy

Cranial Sacral therapy

Expressive Arts Therapy

Family Constellations

Feldenkrais

Hakomi

Massage

Myofascial work/massage

Neurofeedback

Nutritionist and functional medicine practitioners

Osteopathy

Physiotherapy

Play therapy

Reflex integration

Traditional Chinese Medicine

Yoga

TRE and *breathwork* may be helpful, though can be problematic if used at the wrong time, given their propensity for dissociation and tissue damage.

Psychedelic Assisted Therapies are controversial for good reason and still illegal in many countries, though highly recommended by some for being able to break through deep rooted patterns and create radical and far-reaching healing experiences.

Appendix III: Artwork

Arien Barley, Visual Artist and Explorer: instagram.com/arienbarley (p 20, 129)

Anne Marie Hogya, Occupational Therapist and Movement Specialist: annemariehogya.com (p 58)

Davida Taurek: Psychotherapist, 5Rhythms Facilitator, Mindfulness Coach: davidataurek.com (p 120)

Dóra Matyus, Visual Artist: doramatyus.weebly.com (p 51, 89, 107)

Fanny Ducheyne, Visual Artist: fannyducheyne.com, Art Therapist, Watsu-WaterDance Practitioner: dansedescorps.com (p 98)

Gary Dadd, Artist and Illustrator: garydadd.com (p 25, 102, and all practice icons)

Jakub Moulis, Movement Facilitator: embodimentmotion.dance (p 116)

Joëlle Berteaux, Visual Artist: joelleberteaux.weebly.com (p 41, 80, 152)

Julia Knezevic, Movement Teacher, Medicine Woman: dance5rhythms.de (p 125)

Kata Máthé, Dance Teacher and Visual Artist: katamathe.com (p 72, 84)

Katja Mai, Visual Artist: katja.mai@mailbox.org (p 45)

Marc Silvestre, 5Rhythms teacher and coach marcsilvestre.com (p 77)

Marta Carvalho, Visual Artist & Creative Mentor: instagram.com/tokastudio (p 14)

Melanie Schambach, Social Artist, MelanieSchambach.com (p 38)

Dr. Melissa Michaels, Movement Mentor and Artist: goldenbridge.org (p 67)

Rui Miguel, dancer and Visual Alchemist: fixacaoproibida.blogspot.pt (Front cover)

Sarah Rotenberg, Multi-disciplinary Artist interested in Structural Harmonics through Sentient Movement: sarahrotenberg.com (p 11, 49, 148)

Szabó Ivett, Photographer: szaboivett.hu (p159)

Unknown dancers (p 113)

Blessings.... you're on your own, together with everyone....

Adam Barley is a movement catalyst, author, and the founder of ZeroOne, an evolving mystery school based on embodiment, presence and enquiry. He has a world-wide reputation for creating transformative embodiment experiences that combine influences from dance, meditation, voicework, tantra and trauma-informed therapies. For more information about his work, visit adambarley.com.

Lightning Source UK Ltd.
Milton Keynes UK
UKHW051919211222
414204UK00006B/36